FOLENS SCIENCE IN ACTION

CW00536585

Teachers' Resource Book 3

Contents

Environment

4 - 13

Forces

34 - 43

Light, Colour and Sound

14 - 23

Materials

44 - 53

Electricity and Magnetism

24 - 33

Animal Life

54 - 64

Acknowledgements

Folens Publishers would like to thank the headteacher, staff and pupils of St Thomas's Primary School, Blackburn, Morrison Junior School, Liverpool and Mosspits Junior School, Liverpool for their assistance in producing *Science In Action*.

The authors wish to thank Tony Early, Noel George, Mike Speed, Ian Vandewalle, Geoff Hayward, Paul McNie (S.W. Water Services), Pauline Quinn, Spectrum Educational Equipment, Barrie Cooper (RSPB). Special thanks to Vic Powell and family for providing props and posing for photographs.

Folens books are protected by international copyright laws. All rights reserved. The copyright of all materials in this book, except where otherwise stated, remains the property of the publisher and the authors. No part of this publication may be reproduced, stored in a retrieval system, or transmitted in any form, or by any means, for whatever purpose without the written permission of Folens Limited. Folens copymasters do allow photocopying of selected pages of this publication for educational use, providing that this use is within the confines of the purchasing institution. You may make as many copies as you require of the pages indicated.

© 1994 Folens Limited, on behalf of the authors. ISBN 1 85276261 6

First published 1994 by Folens Limited, Albert House, Apex Business Centre, Boscombe Road, Dunstable LU5 4RL.

Editor: Joshua Dubin. Illustrator: Chris Roper. Photographs by Chris Moorcroft, Karen Hartley, Peter Ryan, Natural Science Photos and The Garth Dawson Studios. Printed in Singapore by Craft Print.

Using Science In Action

Science in Action has been specifically designed to meet the needs of primary school teachers and children. It not only covers the Programmes of Study for Key Stages One and Two but unlike the National Curriculum recognises that Nursery and Reception classes are an integral part of the whole school approach to curriculum planning. The themes covered are in a matrix on the rear cover of this book.

AGES 4 TO 7 materials include:
- a *Teachers' Resource Book* for each of the themes covered
- a *Big Book* for each of the three years
- *laminated cards* for children aged 6 - 7 years
- a *Planning and Practice Book* which gives advice and guidance for curriculum planning and assessment.

AGES 7 TO 11 materials are designed to support schools in implementing a **two year rolling programme** of the science strands. Each of the following themes are covered twice across the four years:

BOOKS 1 and 3	BOOKS 2 and 4
Environment	Space
Light, Colour and Sound	Weather
Electricity and Magnetism	Energy
Forces	Plant Life
Materials	Earth, Rocks and Fossils
Animal Life	Our Bodies

PLANNING AND ASSESSMENT
Science In Action provides support before, during and after a science project in all four *Teachers' Resource Books* and in the Key Stage Two *Planning and Practice Book*.

SCIENTIFIC INVESTIGATION
The guidance matrix (page 3) offers examples of *What to look for* when assessing children's performance in these skills. The *Planning and Practice Book* provides additional teacher and pupil support for scientific investigations.

KNOWLEDGE AND UNDERSTANDING
Each theme in the *Teachers' Resource Books* includes a *Planning and Assessment* section which provides detailed coverage of the scientific knowledge and understanding in both the pupil and teacher material. The *Pupil Profile* sheets give examples of *What to look for* as evidence of attainment. The photocopiable *Activity sheets* in the *Teachers' Resource Books* are designed to be used for assessment purposes and can be kept in each child's portfolio.

BACKGROUND INFORMATION
It has been recognised for some time that many primary teachers lack confidence in teaching science because of their lack of scientific knowledge. *Science In Action* explains simply and sometimes in diagrammatic form the knowledge teachers need to support children's investigations.

SCIENCE IN CONTEXT
The authors recognise the need to 'set the scene' for scientific investigations. *Science In Action* provides suggestions for collections, displays, visits and other resources. There is an emphasis throughout on the everyday experiences of children.

CLASSROOM MANAGEMENT
The pupil book pages are arranged in pairs. The left-hand page introduces a real life situation with tasks which are designed to be self-supporting for individuals or groups of children. This will free the teacher from whole class teaching to work with children involved in practical, structured scientific investigations.

DIFFERENTIATION
The material is presented pictorially and in writing whenever possible to support more reluctant readers, and to recall teacher/child discussion more easily. The science activities are presented at different levels. The *Challenger* section on each double page spread is designed to encourage the development of higher order skills and stretch the more able.

RECORDING
A variety of recording methods are suggested throughout *Science In Action*: charts, graphs, pictograms, matrices and others. Children need to be taught how to construct and use these before they can select the most appropriate form of recording to present their findings.

DISCUSSION AND QUESTIONING
Children are encouraged to interpret the results of their investigations. The teachers' material suggests scientific questions which might be asked of children to facilitate productive discussion and further their thinking.

HEALTH AND SAFETY
Warnings appear wherever it is necessary for the children and teachers to TAKE CARE.

Science In Action has been carefully planned to provide structure, background information and ideas for classroom organisation and for a science curriculum where children's progress is systematically assessed and recorded.

Assessing Experimental and Investigative Science

Investigative and Experimental Science

i: Planning experimental procedures.
ii: Obtaining evidence.
iii: Analysing evidence, drawing conclusions and considering evidence.

Skills

1. Turns ideas into investigable forms.
2. Uses trial runs to aid planning.
3. Makes predictions.
4. Uses scientific knowledge and understanding to decide what evidence is needed.
5. Understands and carries out fair tests.
6. Selects and uses appropriate equipment.
7. Repeats observations and measurements to ensure reliability.
8. Records observations and measurements clearly, while working.
9. Makes comparisons.
10. Uses tables, bar charts and line graphs to record findings.
11. Looks for patterns or trends in findings.
12. Judges whether the evidence answers the question.
13. Draws conclusions from findings.
14. Judges whether evidence supports predictions.
15. Explains conclusions in terms of scientific knowledge and understanding.
16. Considers the likelihood of obtaining the same results if the work is repeated.

Pupil profile: Experimental and Investigative Science

Child's name: _____ Date of birth: _____ Date: _____

SKILL	AT	WHAT TO LOOK FOR	COMMENTS (Teacher and child)	
1	1(i)	Suggests how to find out what makes one electromagnet more powerful than another.		
2	1(i)	Places loads in different positions on a lever, while planning an investigation, to find the best position.		
3	1(i)	Predicts that the force needed to lift a load using three pulleys will be less than that needed when using one.		
4	1(i)	Identifies the factors which could affect the strength of an electromagnet. Can test each one in turn.		
5	1(i) (ii)	Plans and carries out a fair test using a collection of fabrics.		
6	1(i) (ii)	Uses computerised sensing equipment to measure and record the intensity of sounds.		
7	1(ii)	Repeats measurements, in Newtons, of the force needed to lift a load using a pulley.		
8	1(ii)	Records forces needed to move sports shoes.		
9	1(iii)	Compares the effects of convex and concave lenses.		
10	1(iii)	Uses a bar chart to record weights supported by bridges.		
11	1(iii)	Notes that the closer wire is coiled, the stronger the electromagnet will be.		
12	1(iii)	Concludes that orange juice is acid because it turns litmus red.		
13	1(iii)	Understands that a large number of algae found in a river water sample indicates that the water may be polluted.		
14	1(iii)	Supports a prediction that brass would not rust, by observing nails of different metals.		
15	1(iii)	Explains that water travelled more quickly up one wick than others because it was more absorbent.		
16	1(iii)	Thinks that one place was found to be 'very noisy' because of unusual events, e.g. roadworks.		

Planning and Assessment: Environment

Knowledge and Understanding of Science:
Science in everyday life.
Health and safety.

AT2 Life and Living Processes
  v: Living things in their environment.
AT3 Materials and their Properties
  i: Grouping and classifying materials.
  iii: Changing materials.

AT4 Physical Processes
  ii: Energy.

AT	SCIENTIFIC CONCEPT	PUPIL MATERIAL	TEACHERS' BOOK PAGE
2(v)	Match of animals and habitats.		9, 10
	Sensitivity in handling and collecting living things.	Should be stressed at all times.	
	How human activity changes the environment.	*The greenhouse effect, The ozone layer, Acid rain, Organic farming, Oil at sea*	11, 12
	Competition between living things.		8, 10
	How pollution affects living things.	*The greenhouse effect*	12
3(i)	Relating materials to everyday uses.		13
	Dangers associated with some everyday materials.	Should be stressed at all times.	
	Weathering of rock.	*Acid rain*	
3(iii)	Waste disposal. The processes causing change.		10, 13
	Solids, liquids and gases.	*The ozone layer*	11
	Acids and alkalis.		10
4(ii)	Combustion of fuel produces waste gases.	*Acid rain*	11
	Burning of fuels in everyday life.		11, 12
	Using energy.		12
4(v)	The limited supply of natural resources.		13

Pupil profile: Environment

Knowledge and Understanding of Science

Child's name: _____

Date of birth: _____ Date: _____

WHAT TO LOOK FOR	COMMENT	AT
Can name some of the animals likely to be found in a pond, a rotting tree stump and a shrubbery.		2(v)
Knows that animals should be returned to their natural habitats.		
Knows that gases from power stations can pollute the air.		
Can name some animals which feed on the leaves from a particular plant.		
Knows that some water dwelling animals can tolerate pollution better than others.		
Can classify metals according to whether they (e.g.) bend, rust, float, are magnetic.		3(i)
Knows that exhaust gases are harmful to people.		
Knows that acid rain dissolves limestone.		
Understands that waste material from homes and industry has to be disposed of.		3(iii)
Knows that ozone is a gas.		
Is able to use universal indicator to test the acidity of rain water.		
Knows that waste gases are produced when fuel is burned in vehicle engines.		4(ii)
Can name some fuels used in the home or used to produce electricity.		
Understands that movement (kinetic energy) can produce electricity.		
Suggests ways in which limited supplies of metals can be conserved, e.g. by recycling.		4(v)

Science In Action: Environment

Teachers' Guide to the Pupil Material

The greenhouse effect   AT2(v)

Scientific Knowledge/Understanding
The temperature of the air inside a greenhouse is higher than that outside it because the Sun's radiation warms the trapped air inside. Human activity, particularly where chemicals are used, produces gases which surround the Earth.
These gases cause an effect similar to that of a greenhouse, trapping the Sun's radiation and therefore increasing the air temperature.

Background Information
Greenhouse gases include carbon dioxide, methane, low level ozone in the air we breathe and CFCs (chlorofluorocarbons). These gases, present in the lower part of the Earth's atmosphere, allow the Sun's short wave radiation through. This is reflected from the Earth as long wave radiation (heat), and cannot easily pass back through the gases. The result is a warmer climate. This is useful to a certain extent as it keeps the Earth warm, but very high levels of these gases could lead to the melting of polar ice and a resulting rise in sea level.
The Earth's average temperature has risen by 0.5°C since 1900. Calculations based on current trends suggest a further increase of 1°C by the year 2025 and 3°C by 3000.

Teacher Interaction/Organisation
The introductory activity asks children to find out about things which are causing global warming. Collect and display leaflets from organisations which promote care for the environment, e.g. Friends of the Earth, Green political parties, Greenpeace and industrial organisations which take active steps to minimise adverse effects on the environment. Also, to provide contrasting viewpoints, include leaflets from industries whose by-products are harmful gases. Leaflets and newspaper and magazine articles are likely to be more up-to-date than many books. Sources of greenhouse gases include some refrigerators, central heating, air conditioning, aerosols and the manufacturing processes of some plastics (particularly expanded polystyrene). See also Teachers' Resource Book 1, It's plastic. Many manufacturers are reducing the CFCs they produce from their factories.
The practical activity provides a way to assess the difference a greenhouse makes to plant growth. Ask the children to note the variables which need to be controlled (kept the same for each group of plants): location, amount of sunlight, amount of water, temperature, space to grow. Can they tell you which variable has changed? The answer: whether or not the plants have a clear plastic cover. The Challenger allows more able children to plan their own investigation. This should reveal that plants can be scorched by excessively hot sunlight. Ask the children if they know how people prevent this happening in their greenhouses. They may have seen a greenhouse with blinds, or where whitewash has been used on some panes of glass. The practical organisation of this activity is simplified if a group of children observes one plant in the same container. They could report their findings to other groups who may be working on a different activity from the Environment section. It is not always necessary for children to take a practical role in every activity. Presenting findings in a way which makes sense to others is an important scientific skill and also provides an opportunity for others to interpret findings from graphs and charts. Class or group discussion are effective ways of achieving this. Lamps, if needed for the Challenger, should be those used in vivaria (available from pet shops and educational suppliers).

The ozone layer   AT2(v)

Scientific Knowledge/Understanding
Ozone is a gas whose presence, high in the Earth's atmosphere, protects us from the harmful rays of the Sun.

Background Information
Ozone is an oxygen based gas. Most of it is found where it is useful: in the stratosphere (see the diagram accompanying the introductory activity in the Pupil Material).
High level ozone filters out much of the Sun's ultraviolet (UV) radiation. Some CFCs destroy ozone and have caused holes to form, allowing harmful ultraviolet radiation through. Ultraviolet radiation is thought to cause skin cancer.
Ozone at a low level in the atmosphere acts as a greenhouse gas. (See the Pupil Material The greenhouse effect.)

Teacher Interaction/Organisation
Provide information in the form of leaflets, newspaper and magazine articles (as described in The greenhouse effect). Encourage discussion of the information from different points of view:
- Which organisations do the children think are likely to play down the effects of ozone destruction and the effects of CFCs?
- Which organisations are more likely to promote public awareness of the harmful effects?

The chart provided for the practical activity suggests the children award points to products for their ozone friendliness (with regard to CFCs). They could also list ways in which we can all help to protect the ozone layer, as suggested in Teachers' Resource Book 1, Air pollution and litter (pages 10, 12-13).

 Some non-CFC propellants are highly flammable. If children are to work without close supervision, tape the caps on to aerosols and warn children that the gases in them are often harmful, especially if inhaled. If in doubt, supervise them closely.

The Challenger gives an opportunity for the children to test their predictions about organisations' attitudes towards the protection of the ozone layer.

Scientific Knowledge/Understanding
Human activity can affect the environment. In this instance it is the effect of waste gases from industry which is examined and discussed. Industrial waste gases in one area can be blown many hundreds of kilometres away and cause damage to the environment.

Background Information
All rain is slightly acidic because carbon dioxide in the atmosphere dissolves in it, forming carbonic acid. As rain falls it can become polluted with gases such as sulphur dioxide (from the burning of coal and oil in power stations and smelters) and nitrogen oxides (from vehicle exhaust) which make it more acidic. The pH value of pure rainwater is about 5.6 and that of acid rain is as low as 2.0.

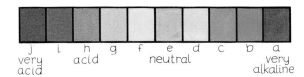

```
  j    i    h    g    f    e    d    c    b    a
very     acid      neutral              very
acid                                    alkaline
```

Teacher Interaction/Organisation
As with the pupil activities for *The greenhouse effect* and *The ozone layer*, leaflets from industrial organisations presenting different points of view will be useful sources of information. The waste products and environmental effects of different methods of power production could be compared. (See also the *Environmental* section of *Teacher Book 1*, Pupil Material *Heating* and *Wind power*.)
Universal indicator, required for the practical activity, is usually supplied in concentrated form. Dilute it with distilled, de-ionised water rather than tap water, which may be either slightly acidic or alkaline and could invalidate the findings. Garages sell distilled water for topping up vehicle batteries and some stores sell it for use in steam irons. This may not be pH neutral. Test its pH and use this as a control.
The pH scale which appears in the Pupil Material is lettered from j to a. This looks as if it is written backwards but has been presented in this way to help children to become familiar with the convention of showing pH values as low for acidic (left on scale) and high for alkaline (right on the scale), yet conforming with normal practice in numbering graphs from low to high (here a to j).

Scientific Knowledge/Understanding
Food production is a human activity which affects the environment.
A farmer's choice of fertiliser and pesticide can affect the water supply.
Fertilisers are used to promote strong and healthy plant growth.

Background Information
Organic matter which fertilises the soil consists of decaying animal and plant material. Chemical fertilisers are made from non-living sources, e.g. nitrates.
Predators such as ladybirds are natural pesticides.
Manufactured pesticides contain natural chemicals which can also kill the pest's natural predators, and may be harmful to people.
Many years ago the natural fertility of the soil was maintained by the rotation of crops. Present day methods, where larger amounts of the same crop are grown on the same land year after year, reduce the fertility of the soil and allow individual species of pests to continue to breed. Crop rotation helps to prevent this, as different crops are attacked by different pests and their natural predators act as pesticides.

Teacher Interaction/Organisation
Provide leaflets from farming organisations, environmental groups such as The Soil Association and associations which promote 'natural' foods. See also Pupil Material *The Greenhouse Effect*.
Can the children think why farmers do not always rotate their crops (grow different crops on the same land each year, sometimes leaving it bare)? One reason is that it can be expensive. The Pupil Material *Prize plants* and *Giants* introduced the idea that people can change the way in which plants grow.

 Close supervision of chemical fertilisers (usually poisonous, often flammable) is needed. Ensure these are stored safely and that children wear protective gloves and wash their hands after this activity.

Draw the children's attention to fair testing. Can they identify the variables (amount of light, water, heat, size of container, etc.) which must be controlled in this investigation?

Scientific Knowledge/Understanding
Human activity can affect the environment. Oil is a natural material which is usually harmless when it remains underground, where it is formed.
Oil floats because it is less dense than water. It can harm animals and plants.
Oil can be removed from the surface of water by scooping it up or using suction. It can be burnt and is dispersed by detergent.

Background Information
Oil is organic and can therefore be broken down by organisms in the sea. Detergents can stop this natural process by killing these organisms.

Teacher Interaction/Organisation
Encourage the children to write to oil producers and environmental organisations (including those concerned specifically with protecting wildlife).
Collect newspaper articles about oil spills at sea which have occurred in the past. (Recent items of news are often available from the newspaper publishers themselves. Older articles may be obtained, sometimes on microfilm/microfiche, from public libraries.)
Ask the children to write to the newspapers and organise a library visit. This will provide an opportunity to develop the children's research skills.

 Avoid engine oils which can irritate the skin. Provide gloves.

Activity sheet: Tree habitat

This food web shows some animals which live, nest or feed, in or under an oak tree. The lines show what each animal eats, e.g. foxes eat sparrows, leaf warblers, robins and squirrels.
(They only eat what is shown below them on the web.)
Use the web to help answer the questions below:

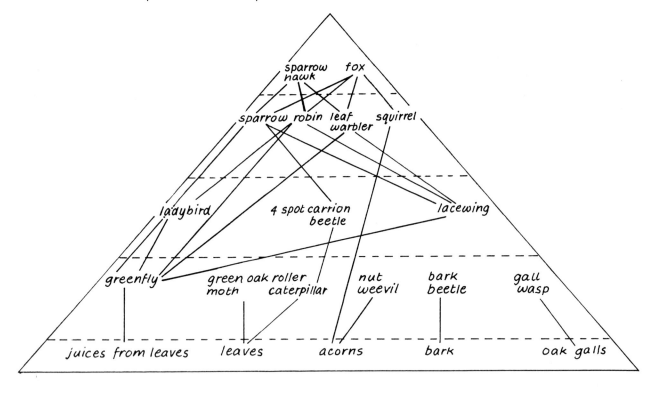

• What do these animals eat?

4 spot carrion beetle ———————— sparrow ————————

nut weevil ———————— ladybird ————————

• What feeds on these?

bark ————————————————————

acorns ————————————————————

greenfly ————————————————————

• What would happen if the tree was sprayed with a pesticide to kill the greenfly?

————————————————————————————

————————————————————————————

Teachers' Notes. (Delete when photocopying. Enlarge to A3.)
This sheet can be used to introduce food webs or to reinforce previous learning. It may also be useful to assess the children's understanding of food chains in an ecosystem and their skills in interpreting information from charts. The structure of this food web may also provide an effective basis for the study of a familiar tree. Reference material based on the local environment may be helpful.

     SIA - Teachers' Resource Book 3. F2616

Living together

Damage to, or removal of, a natural habitat can have unforeseen repercussions. The starting point for this activity is any available ecosystem (i.e. a community and its habitat). Suggestions include: an established tree, pond, hedge, small shrubbery, rotting tree stump or fallen tree.

Before the children begin a survey of animal and plant life in the chosen ecosystem, discuss what difference would be made if the habitat was removed (e.g. for buildings, roads).

Food webs

Food webs show the interdependence of living things in an ecosystem. The following is an example of a simplified food web for a pond:

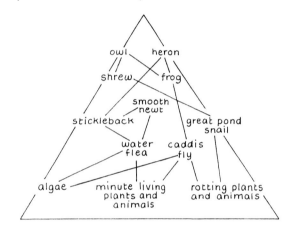

Ask the children what would happen if they collected so many sticklebacks and frog tadpoles that none remained.

Discussion

Background information
People often destroy the habitats and feeding grounds of different species of birds. This can occur when crops are planted right to the edge of fields, leaving no 'headlands' or uncultivated strips around the edges which are sheltered by hedges. When the field is sprayed with fertilisers and pesticides these also destroy any invertebrate life around the field which birds, such as young partridges, need for their survival. Voles, which often live in these headlands, are eaten by barn owls, which are becoming rare in Britain.

Ask the children to construct their own food webs of the ecosystems visited.
What would happen if some of the species found there were removed or destroyed by people?
What would be the result of other animals being introduced into the area?

In the Grand Canyon Game Reserve, deer were protected by wardens who shot their predators (wolves, coyotes and bobcats). Soon there were too many deer for the grass to support. The deer ate shrubs and tree seedlings, changing the habitat. In the end many deer died of starvation. Discuss with the children why this situation occurred and how it could have been prevented.

Waterways

If possible, visit a canal, pointing out to the children that it is not a natural waterway.

 Ensure that there is adequate supervision and that children keep to the paths.

Collect and display photographs and maps of canals. Ask the children how the canal has changed the local environment (other than in physical appearance). What grows there? What lives there?

Test for pollution in a river by counting the separate species of creatures in several samples. Disturb the river bed before taking each sample.

Testing a river for pollution by examining animal life in the water.

Study a local river

Ask the children to look for ways in which people have changed the river.
What is being put into it?
Look for factories discharging waste and pipes releasing sewage. The presence of farm land should also be noted as it could mean that pesticides and nitrates from fertilisers reach the river by seeping into streams. Certain animals and plants cannot survive in polluted waters, e.g. trout and dragonflies. This can be further investigated in a local waterway. (See also *Pupil Book 3*, pages 10-13.) Pollution of water by farming was introduced in *Teacher Book 2*, page 49.
Much can be found out about rivers from maps and photographs.

Can the children explain how dams and other structures have affected the local environment?

Test for acidity

 Wear plastic gloves. Hands should be washed and containers sterilised after use.

This test will reveal the acidity level of a water sample. Readings less than a pH of 5 show that water is abnormally acidic and may be polluted. See also the *Teachers' Notes* accompanying *Acid Rain*.
See also *Pupil Book 3: Acid Rain*, pages 8-9 and *Reactions*, pages 52-53 for further work on acidity.
Teacher Book 2, page 48 introduces the idea of acids in common substances.

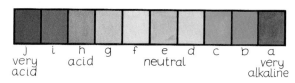

j i h g f e d c b a
very acid   acid   neutral   very alkaline

Discussion

Find out what lives in and around a local river. Sources of information, in addition to first-hand study, include natural history museums, local conservation organisations and wildlife trusts.

Inhabitants of a river
The animals illustrated live in the estuary of the River Mersey, England.
Ask the children to construct food webs for a local river.
Ask what would happen if one species was removed, e.g. by over fishing, or from the effects of pollution.

dog whelk

beadlet anemone

edible periwinkle

edible crab

Traffic

Ask the children what difference the invention of the car has made to the environment.
They could discuss their ideas in groups, and organise displays to present their ideas.

They could collect material from magazines and books about cars past and present.
Help them to find out how vehicle manufacturers try to reduce damage to the environment.
They could present their findings on a chart.

Gas guzzlers

The children could show fuel consumption on a bar chart.
This information is in manufacturers' leaflets.
Can they explain why some cars use more fuel than others?
Is size a factor?

Is speed another factor?

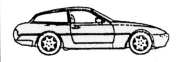

Rubber trees are planted to make the rubber for tyres.

Oil refineries produce fumes.

Car factories produce fumes and smoke.

Tonnes of metal ores are mined to provide vehicle parts.

Motorways cut across the landscape.

Burning fuels give off gases which pollute the air.

We do not use horses as much as we did in the past, so road surfaces are cleaner - no manure is found on them.

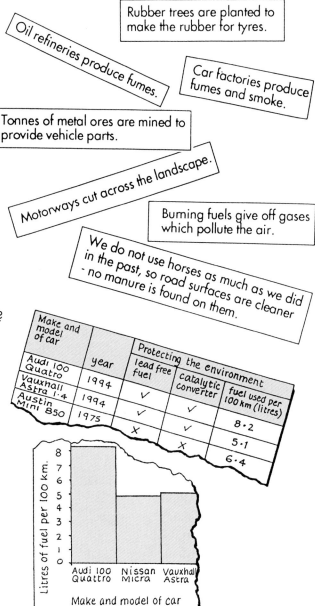

Make and model of car	year	Protecting the environment		
		lead free fuel	catalytic converter	fuel used per 100 km (litres)
Audi 100 Quatro	1994	✓	✓	8·2
Vauxhall Astra 1·4	1994	✓	✓	5·1
Austin Mini 850	1975	✗	✗	6·4

Bar chart — Litres of fuel per 100 km. (vertical axis, 0 to 8); Make and model of car (horizontal axis): Audi 100 Quattro, Nissan Micra, Vauxhall Astra

Roads

Collect and display press cuttings about the construction of new roads.
Ask the children to identify advantages and disadvantages, e.g. if there were no new roads, existing ones could become congested and cause the accumulation of exhaust fumes.
What alternatives to road construction can the children suggest?
What effects will these alternatives have on the environment and the plants and animals living there?
How could the problems be limited or overcome (e.g. by the creation of a 'safe' habitat, inaccessible to people)?
The construction of roads can destroy and divide habitats. This results in new ecosystems being formed, e.g. on roundabouts and verges.

Background information
In a petrol driven vehicle a mixture of petrol and air enters the engine. This is then compressed and ignited by a spark. It is the burning of the petrol which releases the exhaust fumes, including the poisonous gas carbon monoxide. Lead is also emitted in the fumes (with leaded fuel).
A catalytic converter contains a ceramic core with small holes lined with precious metals. It converts the exhaust fumes into mainly harmless gases, such as carbon dioxide, nitrogen and steam. In a diesel vehicle, air alone is taken into the engine. The compression of the air, to about 1/16 of its original volume, causes it to reach a temperature higher than the flash point of the fuel. This causes the fuel to ignite when it is injected into the engine. Waste gases are expelled as exhaust fumes.

Producing energy

Experiments with a hand generator show the children how one form of energy (human movement) can be converted into another (electricity).

Electricity is easily detectable if it is doing work. In this activity the electrical current can be detected by the glow of a light.

Ask the children to plan an investigation to find out about the effects of turning the generator at different speeds.

Remind them to think about fair testing and controls, e.g. use the same bulb and type of paper for each test, hold the paper the same distance from the bulb.

See *Teachers' Resource Book 2*, page 8 for the notes about this method of testing the brightness of a bulb.

Hand generators are available from educational suppliers.

Where did it come from?

Can the children explain where the energy came from to light the bulb?

They have produced electricity from movement.

What other kind of energy did they produce? (Heat: they will feel warm.)

Where did the energy come from to produce their movement? (Food.)

They could draw energy flow charts.

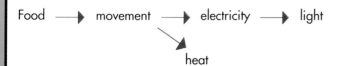

Food ⟶ movement ⟶ electricity ⟶ light
⟶ heat

Science background

Electricity is produced in a variety of ways and from different types of fuel. These methods include:

- using solar cells to convert the Sun's energy into electricity
- using energy released in nuclear fission (splitting the atoms of uranium) to heat water which drives steam turbines
- the use of wind, falling water and tidal flows (hydroelectricity), coal, etc. to drive electrical generators.

Ask the children to consider the advantages and disadvantages of the different methods of producing electricity.

Power and pollution

method	raw material	change to environment	by-products or waste
coal power station	coal	buildings large chimneys subsidence	ash gases heat
nuclear power station	uranium	buildings	radioactive solid, liquid gas, heat material
wind generators	none	many generators on hillsides	noise and some heat
solar energy	none	large solar collectors	heat

Do the children know which raw materials are used for manufactured energy, and which of them (e.g. coal, oil, gas) can also be used directly in homes or factories?

Draw the children's attention to the fact that the production of some forms of energy (e.g. coal and nuclear) results in waste products.

Discuss how the production and use of all forms of energy affects the environment.

Useful sources of information include: electricity generating companies, gas companies, oil refineries, nuclear power stations and coal mining organisations.

See also pages 28-29.

Limited supplies

Metals

Collect and display items made from metal.
Can the children separate them into **ferrous** (made from iron) and **non-ferrous** (not made from iron) metals?

ferrous   non-ferrous

Iron and steel are often recycled. Aluminium is also recycled (see *Pupil Book 1*, pages 32-33).
Branching keys, like the one below, can help children to identify metals.

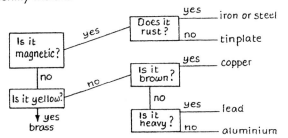

Scrapyards have large magnets to separate ferrous from non-ferrous metals.

Give the children named metal samples to test. Ask them to use their findings to identify the metals in their collection.

metal	colour	Heavy or light?	Does it conduct electricity?	Does it bend easily?	? magnetic	can it be polished?
brass	yellow	heavy	✓	✗	✗	✓
iron	grey	heavy	✓	✗	✓	✗

Water

Introduce the idea that water is a valuable resource. Begin by discussing the water which we use in homes and schools.
Ask the children to plan an investigation into how much water they and their families use for everyday purposes.
Can they think of ways to save water?
How could water be saved? How much?

water use	volume of water	How we could save water	volume saved
washing hands		put a plug in the washbasin	
flushing toilet		put a brick in the cistern	

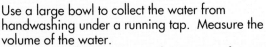

Do not suggest that children reduce the amount of water they drink each day.
This can harm their health.

Flushing

Demonstrate how the cistern works, particularly the ballcock. Mark the water level in a full cistern.
Empty the cistern by flushing. Prevent it from refilling by holding up the ballcock.
Measure water in the cistern up to the water level mark.
Ask the children to suggest methods of reducing the amount of water used each time they flush.
They could think of ways to fill part of the space in the cistern with something other than water.
Many people place a brick in the cistern.
The children could find the volume of water displaced by a brick.

Washing hands

Use a large bowl to collect the water from handwashing under a running tap. Measure the volume of the water.
The children should estimate the amount of water needed to wash their hands. They should put this water in a bowl or wash basin and record its volume.
Ask them to compare the volumes.

Planning and Assessment: Light, Colour and Sound

Knowledge and Understanding of Science:
Science in everyday life.
Health and safety.

AT4 Physical Processes
iv: Sound.
v: Light.

AT	SCIENTIFIC CONCEPT	PUPIL MATERIAL	TEACHERS' BOOK PAGE
4(iv)	How sound travels through solids and air.	*Sound tubes*	
	Echoes.		19
	Measuring the intensity of sound.		21
	Noise pollution.		21
4(v)	Effects produced by shining light through transparent blocks.	*Tricks with light*	18
	Effects of light travelling through water.	*Tricks with light*	
	Effects of light travelling through lenses.	*Magnifying*	22-23
	Magnifying.	*Magnifying*	22-23
	Combinations of lenses.		22
	Effects of shining lights through prisms.		18
	Effects of colour filters on light.	*Colour quest*	
	Mixing coloured paints.	*Colour quest*	
	Mixing coloured light.	*Colour quest*	18
	Speed of light and sound.	*Thunder and lightning*	

Pupil profile: Light, Colour and Sound

Knowledge and Understanding of Science

Child's name: _____

Date of birth: _____ Date: _____

WHAT TO LOOK FOR	COMMENT	AT
Knows that sounds travel more clearly through solids than through air.		4(iv)
Can describe that sounds are reflected off hard materials.		
Can use computer sensing equipment to measure the intensity of sound.		
Can name sounds which cause noise pollution.		
Knows that light changes direction as it travels through a perspex block.		4(v)
Describes how objects look when resting in water.		
Knows that some combinations of lenses make distant objects look nearer.		
Understands that prisms split light into the colours of the spectrum and can name these colours.		
Understands that colour filters allow only light of the same colour to pass through.		
Can describe how to mix paint using the three primary colours.		
Is able to compare the mixing of coloured lights to form other colours with the mixing of paint colours.		
Explains that we see lightning before we hear thunder because light travels faster than sound.		
Knows that lenses can be used to magnify.		
Understands that lenses can be used to help the eye to focus.		

Science In Action: Light, Colour and Sound

Teachers' Guide to the Pupil Material

Tricks with light | AT4(v)

Scientific Knowledge/Understanding
Light is bent (**refracted**) as it passes through water and other transparent materials.
The children should first be introduced to the idea that light travels in straight lines (see *Teachers' Resource Book 1, Travelling light*).

Background Information
At the point where light meets water, or another transparent medium, it is refracted. As rays of light enter or leave a block of perspex, glass, or an expanse of water they change direction but continue to travel in straight lines.

A paintbrush in water looks bent because the light, which is reflected from it, bends as it passes from the water and through the air. (We see things only if they reflect light: see *Teachers' Resource Book 1, Travelling light*.)

Teacher Interaction/Organisation
The introductory activity draws attention to a familiar phenomenon: that objects in water often look bent. In the picture, Jordan misses the coin with the stick because the light reflected from it bends as it leaves the water, making the coin appear to be in a different place. The children should notice that the stick appears to bend where it enters the water.
Ensure that children take care with the sticks.
The practical investigation shows the effects of light passing through a transparent block and encourages careful observation.
The following illustrates the direction of the rays of light passing through different transparent blocks which may be noticed:

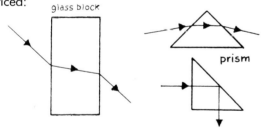

The direction of the refracted light rays depends upon the angle at which the light originally hit the transparent block. It is possible, with some blocks, that no light at all will leave. Instead it is refracted internally (**total internal refraction**):

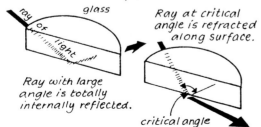

A darkened area in which to observe the effects of the light makes the beams more obvious. The children could place the light box inside a large carton with its open side facing them. Battery powered light boxes, available from educational suppliers, are safer than mains powered ones. They are also easier to use in a primary classroom which may be short of suitably positioned electrical points.

> If a mains powered light box is used it must be connected to an adaptor. Most use 12 volts.

Magnifying | AT4(v)

Scientific Knowledge/Understanding
Curved lenses can be used to give a magnified image of an object.
Combinations of different pairs of **convex** and **concave** lenses produce a variety of effects. These effects are useful for different purposes which have applications in everyday life.

Background Information
Single convex lenses are used in magnifying lenses and are used for a magnified reading glass. The microscope has a pair of convex lenses:

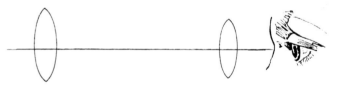

Note: spectacles do not necessarily magnify an image. Their lenses help the eyes to focus. Explanations of the ways in which lenses work become very complex and simplification may be confusing. It is more important that children are aware of the effects of particular pairs of lenses placed at measured distances from each other. They should be encouraged to observe, measure and record.
Warn children not to look directly at the sun through lenses.

Teacher Interaction/Organisation
Ask the children to think of everyday uses of lenses. The introductory activity in the Pupil Material illustrates some of these uses.
The practical activity shows the children the importance of the distance of an object from a magnifying lens, and helps them to find the **focal length** of lenses (distance at which objects are seen 'in focus' and magnified).
Do not try to explain the working of lenses; instead, the effects of lenses of different types can be observed and recorded by the children. These can then be related to their everyday uses. Some simple uses of lenses were introduced in the Pupil Material, *The Moon (Space)*.

The *Challenger* suggests the children plan an investigation to find the differences between thick and thin bulging (convex) lenses.

The amount of 'bulge' of a lens, together with the ability of the glass/perspex from which it is made to refract light, will have an effect on its strength. Clear glass marbles, for instance, are very efficient magnifiers as they have an extremely wide bulge.

Colour quest   AT4(v)

Scientific Knowledge/Understanding
Coloured transparent materials filter out light of all but their own colour.

Background Information
Stained glass windows do not give light any colour. Each coloured pane filters out all but its own coloured light, e.g. red allows only red light to pass, green allows only green light through.

Mixing coloured light is different from mixing coloured paints as the primary colours of light are red, blue and green. These combine to produce a yellowish colour. However, these colours when mixed as paint produce brown.

The more colours of paint added to a mixture, the darker it becomes but the more colours of light which are combined, the lighter it becomes.

All colours of the spectrum combined produce white light.

Teacher Interaction/Organisation
This activity could be carried out effectively in conjunction with *Over the rainbow* (page 18).

If possible, visit a church or another building with stained glass windows and encourage the children to observe and explain the effects of light. They may think that the glass adds colour to white light.

Remind the children of the colours of the spectrum (violet, indigo, blue, green, yellow, orange and red) and ask them which of those colours each pane of glass is allowing through.

The practical activity encourages exploration of the effects of colour combinations using filters.

Draw the children's attention to the differences between these mixtures of coloured light and the mixtures of the same colours of paint. The colours produced, if high quality filters are used, are:

- red + green = yellow

- red + blue = magenta (purple)

- blue + green = cyan (blue/green).

Green light cannot be made from other colours as it is a primary colour of light. It can be produced using paints by combining blue and yellow as it is not a primary colour of pigment or paint.

The *Challenger* asks the children to predict the effects of combinations of colour filters. The more filters that are used, the more the light is filtered out.

'Correct' colour filters are available from stage and theatrical suppliers as well as educational or scientific suppliers. Local secondary schools may also be able to provide stage-lighting offcuts.

Thunder and lightning   AT4(iv) (v)

Scientific Knowledge/Understanding
Light travels faster than sound.
We see an event which makes a sound before we hear it.

Background Information
Light travels at about 300 million metres per second and sound at 330-340 metres per second, in the air.

This explains why we see lightning before we hear thunder. The further away the storm is, the greater the gap between seeing lightning and hearing thunder.

Thunderstorms are caused by electrical charges in the clouds. The energy that is produced by these charges escapes as light and sound. They occur simultaneously.

Teacher Interaction/Organisation
If possible, before the children begin the introductory activity, show them a video featuring several thunderstorms recorded from different distances.

- What do they notice about the timing of thunder and lightning?
- Can they explain why they see the lightning first?

The practical activity **could** be approached as follows (if space and supervision allow):
Find a large open space, e.g. a playing field, a park or a long, straight footpath.
Position two groups of children 660m apart.
Group A sends signals to group B, using both a visible signal (e.g. waving a piece of card/fabric) and a loud sound simultaneously.
Some of group B indicate when they see the visible signal; others, with their backs to group A, indicate when they hear the sound.
The sound should take 2 seconds to travel from group A to group B. The visible signal should be seen immediately.

Sound tubes   AT4(iv)

Scientific Knowledge/Understanding
Hard materials conduct sound more efficiently than soft ones.

Background Information
Soft materials absorb sound. Hard materials reflect it.

Teacher Interaction/Organisation
The introductory activity asks the children to examine the parts and function of a stethoscope.

If possible provide a real stethoscope (available from educational suppliers) for the children to try.

Draw their attention to the funnelled shape of the end which is placed on the patient's back or chest. This collects sound from a wide area and directs it to a narrower one, making the instrument more efficient than the naked ear.

The practical activity encourages the children to consider the variables involved when experimenting with stethoscopes they have made. They should isolate only one variable to change at a time, e.g. length of the tube, material of the tube. They are likely to find harder materials more efficient conductors of sound than soft ones.

Over the rainbow

When sunlight or bright artificial light strikes oil on the surface of water, a rainbow effect may be seen. This is because the white light has been split into the colours of the spectrum.

Collect and display materials for simulating rainbows:

The most successful ways to show light splitting into the colours of the spectrum are:

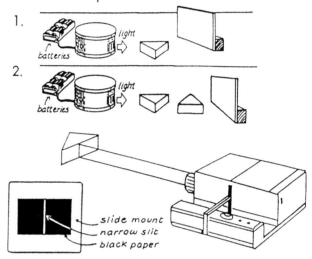

Sometimes a rainbow can be produced this way. Experiment with moving the card and mirror into different positions to find the most effective place.

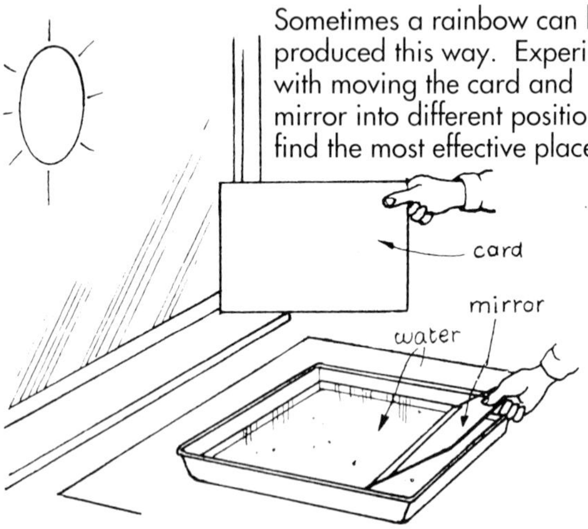

card

mirror

water

slide mount

narrow slit

black paper

Use a projector with a slide prepared as here. Shine the beam through a prism.

Discussion

Background information
The shorter a wave length is, the more it is bent (refracted) by a transparent medium, e.g. water, glass, perspex. Violet light has the shortest waves of light in the visible spectrum, and so is bent most. A prism bends the white light passing through it in such a way that it is splitting its seven main colours. Drops of water can produce the same effect as a prism.
If this light is then shone through a second prism, refraction combines these colours again to make white light.

Ask the children to notice the order in which the colours of the spectrum appear. Is it always the same? Do they notice which colour bends the most?
Ask the children to compare the spectrums of light they created in their experiments with natural ones (rainbows). Photographs of rainbows are useful for this.
The children may only observe six colours, as indigo is difficult to see.
Ask the children to predict what will happen if they shine the light emerging from a prism through filters of different colours. Can the children plan an investigation to find out? Do they notice which colours are allowed to pass through each filter? (Filters are introduced in *Teachers' Resource Book 1*, page 17.)
What do the children think will happen if the split up light emerging from one prism then passes through another?
They may need help with this. The beam of light can be produced by placing a mask with a narrow slit over a projector, as shown above.

Echoes

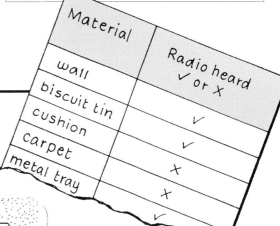

Name:Material	Number:cm
A plastic	6
B carpet	0
C sponge	1
D metal	8
E foil	3
F cork	0

Ask the children to list places where they have heard echoes: caves, tunnels, empty rooms, swimming baths, hard shoes in corridors.

Discuss places where no echoes are heard.

What do they think makes sounds echo in some places but not in others? The children might have noticed that sounds echo in empty rooms, but when rooms contain furniture, carpets and curtains, this does not happen. What do they think makes the difference?

Can the children plan an investigation to find out? They could use a large metal or wooden box and record sounds made inside the box, then repeat the activity after lining the box with soft material, e.g. cotton wool.

Listening to echoes

Set up the equipment as illustrated below:

Material	Radio heard √ or X
wall	
biscuit tin	√
cushion	√
carpet	X
metal tray	X
	√

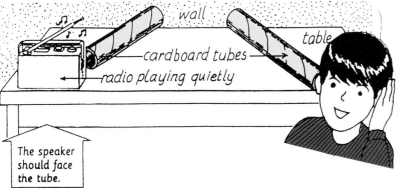

wall

table

cardboard tubes

radio playing quietly

The speaker should face the tube.

Do the children think they will hear the radio? With which ear?

Ask them to try out the investigation and draw a picture to show how the sound travels to the ear. The tubes could be pointed at different materials. Try to ensure that the children have a quiet place to carry out this investigation.

Discussion

How would the results of the activity above be different if tubes of a different material were used, e.g. stiff plastic pipes, metal pipes?

Ask them to plan a fair test to find out. Can they also find a way to measure the volume of the echoes?

(The ACTIVITY SHEET: *Planning sheet*, page 20 may be useful.)

Variables to control include: length and width of tubes/pipes, background noise, volume of the radio.

The variable to change is the distance of the listening tube from the reflecting surface. This can be used as a measure of loudness.

Before proceeding discuss with the children how loudly the radio should be played: quietly, otherwise the distances could be vast.

Science background

Sound travels as waves through air (and other gases), solids and liquids. This material vibrates. Sound cannot travel through a vacuum because there is nothing to vibrate. Soft materials do not reflect sound because they do not vibrate.

 Children should not put anything in their ears except a purpose made ear plug, if appropriate.

Activity sheet: Planning sheet

What we are trying to answer

_____

_____

_____

_____

_____

_____

We will need:

_____

_____

_____

_____

Investigate...

What we will do

What we will observe, measure or count

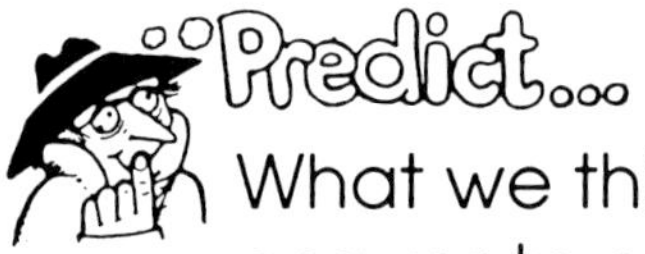

What we will keep the same

Predict...

What we think will be the answer to our question

What we will change

Teachers' Notes. (Delete when photocopying.)
This sheet provides one way for the children to plan their investigations. It is designed to help them to plan fair tests, and encourages the children to observe, question, predict and measure. The sheet also allows them to identify any variables which they will need to control.

Too noisy

This investigation could be effectively combined with activities from the *Environment* section of this book.
An introductory activity is to ask the children to list very noisy things in the environment. In groups of four the children could then produce from these lists a set of twelve cards, each labelled with something noisy. Ask them to order the cards: quietest to loudest.

Which do the children think is louder?
How can they find out?

One way is to tape record the sounds and use a computer to monitor their volume.

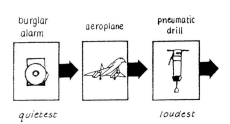

burglar alarm → aeroplane → pneumatic drill

quietest   *loudest*

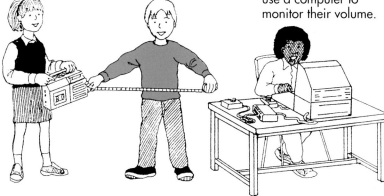

Background information
Sound intensity is measured in decibels. Continuous exposure to sounds over 80 decibels can damage the hearing.
The energy carried by a sound wave determines its loudness.

 soft sound   loud sound

Examples of the intensity of familiar sounds: barely audible - 0dB, whisper - 20dB, conversational speech - 60dB, pneumatic drill 90-95dB, rock concert - 110dB, jet plane taking off - 120 dB.

Using sensing equipment

To record and monitor the volume of sounds the following equipment is needed in addition to the computer:
● interface
● sound sensor
● software which records sound intensity (most of the software available will represent the sound numerically, as a chart and as a graph)
● printer (to provide a record for display purposes).
This activity will help the children to understand that the intensity of sound is measured in decibels.

Ask them to make sure their test is fair, perhaps using the ACTIVITY SHEET: *Planning sheet*, on page 20.
Two variables which the children could consider are:

● Sounds should be recorded and played back from similar distances.
● The volume control of the tape recorder should be kept constant.

Noise or music?

What some people would call noise is music to others. Whatever type of music it is, however, it consists of sounds of different frequencies (high and low notes).
Ask the children to identify the sounds in the environment they find pleasant/unpleasant.

Can they detect beats or rhythms in different sounds, e.g. clocks ticking, windscreen wipers, a heart beating? A heartbeat can be recorded using a microphone pressed to the chest.
Ask the children to listen for repetitions of sequences, e.g. in bird song, pieces of music, church bells.

Investigating lenses

Collect and display a selection of lenses. Include large and small lenses, **concave**, **convex**, **biconcave**, **biconvex** and lenses of different central thicknesses:

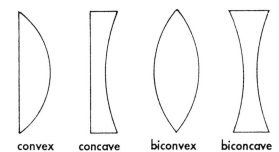

convex   concave   biconvex   biconcave

The children could experiment to find the effects of different combinations of pairs of lenses.
Can they discover which combinations of lenses are best for telescopes and microscopes?
Very able children could use their findings to complete a chart like this:

Show the children everyday objects which make use of lenses. Ask them what the lens does in each.

- Does it make an image which is bigger or smaller than the real thing?
- Does it give the viewer a wider or a narrower view?

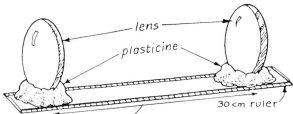

This distance will need adjusting until a clear image is seen. A longer ruler or piece of wood may be needed.

Pairs of lenses						Image seen
Lens nearer to the eye			Lens further from the eye			
Type	Diameter cm	Bulge fat/thin	Type	Diameter cm	Bulge fat/thin	
Convex			Convex			
Convex			Convex			

They could try combinations of three lenses.
What everyday uses could these have?
Concentrate on *what* lenses do and how we use them, rather than *how* they work.

Optical instruments

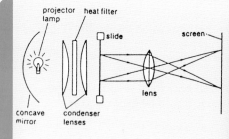

Can the children demonstrate how a slide projector works?
One method is to shine a very bright light through a slide with a biconvex lens in front of it. If the image is projected on to a screen it will be easier for the children to see the effect.

Background information
Microscope
This instrument is used to magnify small objects which are close to the viewer. It is designed with two convex lenses (biconvex) and therefore has a 'fat bulge'. The result is an image which is seen, not only magnified, but also upside down.

Telescope
An astronomical telescope has two lenses. The lens which is nearer the object viewed bulges less than the one near the viewer. This enables the astronomer to see objects some distance away. See *Teachers' Resource Book 2*, page 6 for a further explanation.

Slide projector
Light is collected by the concave mirror and then reflected through the condenser. This spreads the light evenly on the slide. The diagram shows this effect by illustrating the rays of light from two points on the slide. It also shows that the image is inverted on the screen.

In focus

Provide a collection of **convex** and **biconvex** lenses of different sizes and with different central thicknesses. Include condenser lenses and clear glass marbles of different sizes.

Ask the children to use the lenses to magnify very small print, e.g. from a telephone directory.
Can they measure the focal lengths (the distance at which the object is in focus and is magnified) of each of the lenses?
Ask them to record their findings.
A chart may be the most suitable method.
Can the children find a pattern to link the central thickness of a lens to its focal length?
Lenses with a thickly bulging centre usually have a shorter focal length than thin lenses.

The children could use a clinometer or Vernier calliper to measure the thickness at the centre of the lenses:

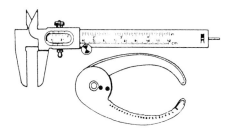

Lens focus/enlarge distance

	Thickness (mm)	Dist. (cm)
A	5	70
B	7	63
C	8	60
D	15	40

A clear glass marble magnifies and is in focus when it is actually touching the object.

magnified

Home-made lenses

Lenses may be made by filling clear, cylindrical containers with water. Which of these do the children think will magnify the most? Ask them to plan an investigation to find out.
The wider the jar, the greater the magnification.

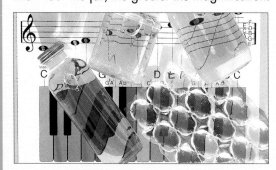

Background information
Explanation of the workings of lenses is very complex. Do not try to explain this to children.
The activities on these pages show them that the central thickness of a lens affects both its magnification and its focal length. If the children find any anomalies this could be due to the refracting quality of the glass, perspex, etc. These can make a difference.
In general, convex lenses are used to magnify. However, this is only when the object viewed is placed within the focal length of the lens:

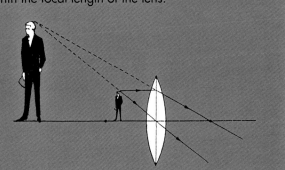

The image is magnified and the correct way up.

Planning and Assessment: Magnetism and Electricity

Knowledge and Understanding of Science:
Science in everyday life.
Health and safety.

AT4 Physical Processes
i: Electricity.
ii: Energy.

AT	SCIENTIFIC CONCEPT	PUPIL MATERIAL	TEACHERS' BOOK PAGE
4(i)	Poles of magnets.	*Poles apart*	
	Compasses.	*Poles apart*	33
	The Earth's magnetic field.	*Poles apart*	
	Magnetic effects of an electric current.	*Electromagnet*	33
	Making magnets.	*Poles apart*	
	Varying the flow of an electric current in a circuit.	*Current control*	28
	Using circuit diagrams.		30, 31
	The dangers of mains electricity.	Should be stressed at all times.	
	Short circuits.	*Short circuits*	
	'Two way' switches.		31
	Using sensing equipment.	*Control it!*	32-33
	Logic gates.	*Control it!*	32-33
4(ii)	Using electricity as a power source for movement.		28-29
	Sources of electrical power.		28-29
	Batteries as stored energy.		29

Pupil profile: Magnetism and Electricity

Knowledge and Understanding of Science

Child's name: _____

Date of birth: _____   Date: _____

WHAT TO LOOK FOR	COMMENT	AT
Understands that magnets have north and south poles; that like poles repel and opposite poles attract each other.		4(i)
Knows that a compass needle is a magnet.		
Knows that north-seeking poles of compasses and magnets point towards the Earth's magnetic north.		
Makes a magnet by stroking an iron/steel nail or pin with a magnet.		
Uses a pencil 'lead' as a 'dimmer switch' (variable resistor).		
Records a circuit in drawing or diagram form. Constructs a circuit from a diagram.		
Knows that mains electricity is dangerous because of its high voltage.		
Knows that electricity follows the easiest route, which may not be the shortest.		
Constructs a circuit with two switches.		
Uses a reed switch or light dependent resistor.		
Makes a circuit where two or more conditions have to be true in order for it to work.		
Uses a solar cell to power an electric motor.		
Can name some fuels used in the home or used to produce electricity.		4(ii)
Knows that sunlight and batteries are sources of electrical power.		
Knows that a battery produces electricity by a chemical reaction.		

Science In Action: Magnetism and Electricity

Teachers' Guide to the Pupil Material

Poles apart   AT4(i)

Scientific Knowledge/Understanding
Magnets have north and south poles.
Opposite poles attract.
Like poles repel each other.
Compass needles are magnets, whose poles point in the same direction as the poles of the Earth. (This will only happen if the needle is allowed to move freely.)
Pieces of iron or steel can be made into temporary magnets by stroking them with a magnet, in one direction.

Background Information
Magnetic materials can be imagined as being made from many tiny magnets, all facing in different directions:

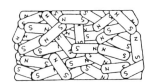

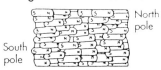

Magnets are also made up of these tiny magnets, but they all face in the same direction whatever the shape of the magnet.

When a magnet attracts a magnetic material it causes the tiny magnets in that material to line up with the south pole in contact with the magnet's north pole:

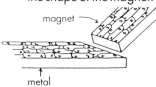

Compasses are magnets whose north poles (actually **north-seeking** poles) point towards the Earth's magnetic north. This is near, but not quite in the same place as the North Pole:

Stroking a piece of steel or iron with a magnet causes the small magnets to line up with their north poles all facing in the same direction.

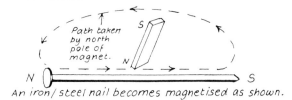

An iron/steel nail becomes magnetised as shown.

Teacher Interaction/Organisation
The introductory activity allows the teacher to assess the children's understanding of magnetism, based on any previous experience. (See *Teachers' Resource Book 1, All kinds of magnets*, page 31, and *North and south*, page 33.)

Compasses can be damaged if kept next to magnets for any length of time. Avoid directly touching compasses with magnets and store them separately.
The practical activity requires the children to investigate one of the variables from the introductory activity: the direction in which the nail or needle is stroked. They can find out about its effect on the end: whether it becomes a north or south pole. To ensure it is a fair test the children should use the same **pole** (end) of the magnet.

Electromagnet   AT4(i)

Scientific Knowledge/Understanding
Magnetism can be produced using electricity.
Factors which affect the strength of an electromagnet include:
-   the number of wire coils
-   the voltage of the battery.

Background Information
An electric current passing through a wire causes a magnetic field to be created around it.
For example, if an iron nail is placed inside a coil of wire, it will become an electromagnet while the current flows. This happens because the small magnets, of which the nail is made, are realigned in the magnetic field that the coil produces.
Electromagnets made from soft iron become temporary magnets. They lose their magnetism when the current is removed. Electromagnets made from hardened steel retain their magnetism for longer. This is because the small magnets tend to stay aligned for longer in steel than in iron.

Teacher Interaction/Organisation
The introductory activity provides an opportunity for the teacher to find out what ideas the children may already have about electromagnets.
The children's answers to the questions can be compared with their results in the practical activity. In this activity they are asked to investigate what effect the number of coils of wire has on the strength of an electromagnet.
Some children may be able to complete the investigation without the instructions provided.
The *Challenger* is a more complex activity which suggests that the children plan and carry out investigations into any of the variables they can think of.
They should discover that a more powerful magnet can be produced by:
-   a higher voltage
-   more coils of wire, and
-   winding the coils more closely.

 Warn the children that electromagnets can get hot. Disconnect the electromagnet as soon as possible.

Short circuits   AT4(i)

Scientific Knowledge/Understanding
An electric current usually follows the easiest route.
This is not necessarily the shortest route but the one where there is least resistance.
If it can flow from one terminal of a battery to another without doing work, such as lighting a bulb, it will.
It will not flow along an unconnected wire.

Background Information
A **short circuit** is the path which offers the least resistance to an electric current.
In the short circuits shown in the Pupil Material, the electricity flows from one terminal of the battery to the other, without doing any work. This causes the battery to become hot and is why any short circuit should be disconnected immediately. A fuse consists of a thin wire inserted in a circuit. A short circuit causes overheating and the fuse burns through. This results in the circuit breaking.

Teacher Interaction/Organisation

> Very close supervision is essential to ensure that short circuits do not remain connected.
> Point out this danger to children. Do not use rechargeable batteries.

Previous experience of making electrical circuits is advisable. *Teachers' Resource Book 1*, pages 26-33 suggests some suitable introductory activities.

Current control   AT4(i)

Scientific Knowledge/Understanding
Some materials conduct electricity better than others.
The ability of a material to conduct electricity can be varied. When this occurs, a **variable resistor** is produced.
Variable resistors have useful everyday applications, e.g. in dimmer switches for lights and in the volume controls of radios and televisions.

Background Information
All materials offer some resistance to electricity. Those which offer least resistance are often called **conductors**, while those which offer most resistance are called **insulators**.
The lead of a pencil (graphite) conducts electricity but not as well as metals, such as steel and copper. The greater the distance travelled by the current along a piece of graphite, the greater the resistance. Materials used in dimmer switches and volume controls behave in the same way.

Teacher Interaction/Organisation
The introductory activity presents **rheostats** (variable resistors) in an everyday context. The children are asked to explain how they think the switches are useful. This leads on to the practical activity where they make their own variable resistors. Encourage the children to use the terms **resistor**, **variable resistor** and **rheostat**. Do they have any of these in their homes? The practical investigation should demonstrate that the greater the distance between the wires on the ends of the pencil lead, the dimmer the bulb will become.
The *Challenger* asks the children to measure and compare the brightness of bulbs as the distance between the ends of the wires is increased. One method is to look at the bulb through layers of thin paper. Begin with one sheet and record the number of layers that can be added until the light is no longer seen. Variables to control include:
- distance from the bulb to the paper
- distance from the eye to the bulb
- type of paper.

Control it!   AT4(i)

Scientific Knowledge/Understanding
A switch is used to join or break an electrical circuit.
Special kinds of switches respond to particular conditions to automatically join or break a circuit.
The **reed** switch is operated by a magnet which closes the gap between two pieces of steel.
The **photo sensor**, or light dependent resistor, acts as a variable resistor. It varies the resistance in the circuit depending on the brightness of the light shining on it: dimmer light ——▷ lower resistance ——▷ brighter bulb.
In a circuit where there is a reed switch, both switches have to complete the circuit for the bulb to light.

Teacher Interaction/Organisation
The introductory activity introduces different types of switches. (Further activities are provided in *Teacher Book 1, Switched on*, page 30 and *Switch on the light*, page 28.)
The answers to the activity are:
- In picture 1 there is no magnet to operate the reed switch and the light will therefore be off.
- In 2, the bright light prevents the photo sensors from completing the circuit and the light will remain off.
- In 3, although the metal strips are connected in the reed switch, the bright light prevents the photo sensors from completing the circuit and the light remains off.
- In 4, the connections are all made to complete the circuit and the light will be on.
In this activity the children are introduced to **and/not** gates: the circuits will only work if certain conditions are present/ not present or if one condition and another are present:
1. If the magnet is present the bulb lights.
2. If light is not present the bulb lights.
3. & 4. If the magnet is present and light is not present the bulb lights.
Where do the children think these bulbs are useful in everyday life? Some may have security lights which switch on when it is dark. (See page 32, *Inputs and outputs*.)
Extension work could include the use of computer software and an interface which allows the use of various switches for control. (Page 21, *Too noisy*, introduces the use of sound sensors.)
The pressure pad, required for the *Challenger* activity, completes the circuit as a toy car passes over it. This results in the light being switched on. The circuit can be designed like this:

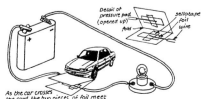

As the car crosses the card the two pieces of foil meet joining the circuit.

Electrical sources

 Warn the children not to play with mains electricity.

Solar electricity

Ask the children to investigate the use of solar cells in circuits. Some can be used to power very small motors. Can they find out which other small electrical items they will power?

Small encapsulated solar cells are available from educational suppliers.

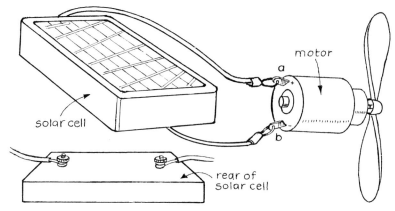

solar cell

motor

a
b

rear of solar cell

Solar cells of different sizes

Ask the children to investigate solar cells of different sizes. Do large cells make a motor turn more quickly than smaller ones?
Ensure that the children carry out a fair test by using the same bulb each time. (Connect the solar cell's terminals **a** and **b** to the motor.)
Can they think of a way to measure the speed of the motor?
They could count the turns of a propeller attached to the motor.

Discussion

Background information
Solar cells are made from highly purified silicon.
The crystals of this silicon have been treated so that they have an electrical charge.
An increase in the amount of solar power can be achieved by:

● using a greater number of cells
● increasing the size of the cells
● increasing the level of light that falls on the cells.

Compare solar power with electricity produced by other methods. Can the children think of any disadvantages of solar electricity? Ask them to predict what would happen if the sunlight was not very bright. They could cover the solar cell with layers of tissue paper.
Can the children plan an investigation to measure the effects of progressively reducing the amount of sunlight reaching the solar cell? The ACTIVITY SHEET: *Planning sheet*, page 20, may help. They could:

● measure the brightness of a bulb powered by a solar cell
● record the amount of time taken by a motor to lift a small weight.

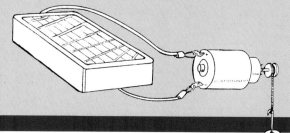

Batteries

Ask the children to suggest what they think is inside a battery. How do they think the electricity is made? Ask them to use drawings to explain their ideas.

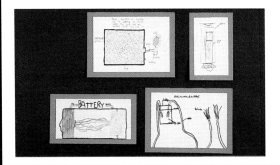

Warn children not to try to cut open batteries. Show them a cut open battery sealed in a transparent container, or a photograph such as the one above.

Lemon battery

Ask the children if they believe that a lemon can be used as a battery.
Can they plan an investigation to find out?
Ask them to make a circuit with a small motor but to replace the battery with a lemon.
The lemon should be rolled/squeezed first.

Do the children think more lemons will make the motor turn faster? A piece of card or paper could be attached to the motor's spindle, and marked, in order to facilitate the counting of its revolutions.
(The motor must be the thin type shown in the drawing; the experiment will not work with the taller, cylindrical type of motor.)

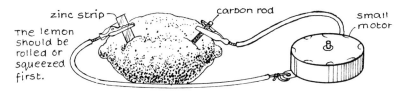

zinc strip   carbon rod   small motor

The lemon should be rolled or squeezed first.

Discussion

Electricity from food

Ask the children to compare the power of a potato, an apple, an orange and a lemon.
Can they plan a fair test to find out which provides the most power, i.e. highest voltage? Just as a circuit with more batteries joined in series makes a motor turn faster, increasing the number of lemons in a circuit has the same effect.
Why do they think that one type of food makes a better battery than another?

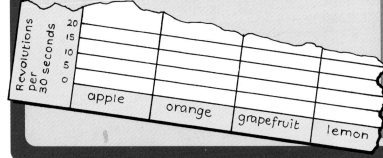

Background information
Energy is never 'used up'. It can be:

* converted into other kinds of energy: heat, movement, light, sound.
* transferred from one thing to another, e.g. wheels turning other wheels, heat sources making other things hot.

The reaction of two metals (e.g. carbon and zinc) with an acid produces the electrical current in a battery. Some foods contain weak solutions of acids which help to produce an electric current. The stronger the acid the higher the voltage. Strictly speaking, a single battery is called a cell, but in everyday usage it is called a battery. A battery consists of two or more cells.

Activity sheet: Circuit diagrams

Name: _____

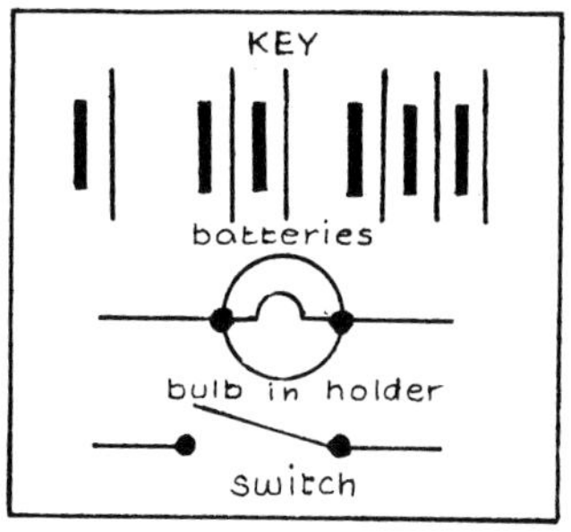

- Draw a picture of each circuit, to show how you would make it.
- Predict what will happen in each circuit.
- Make the circuits.
- Record what happens.

KEY

batteries

bulb in holder

switch

1. 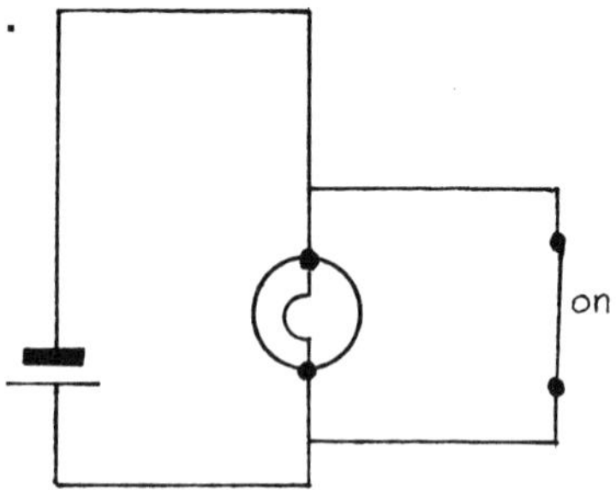	Prediction:	Drawing
on		
What happened:		

2. 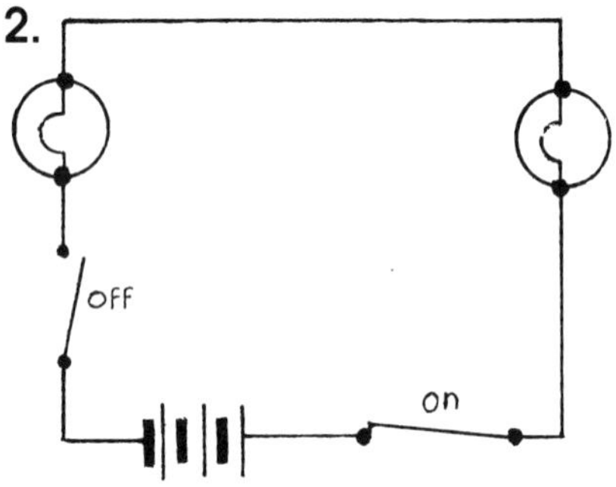	Prediction:	Drawing
off on		
What happened:		

3. 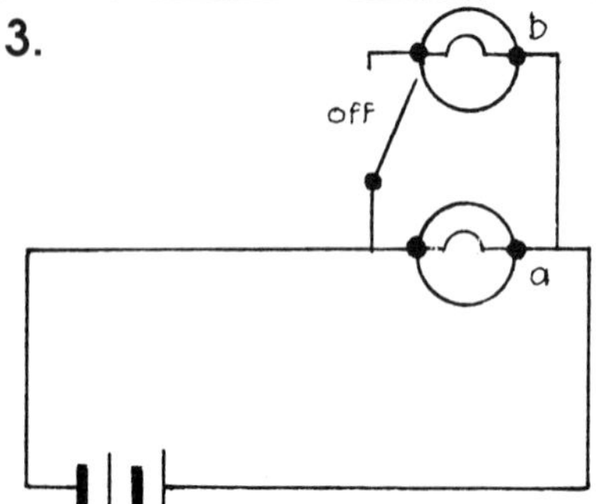	Prediction:	Drawing
off b a		
What happened:		

Teachers' Notes. (Delete when photocopying. Enlarge to A3.)
The children's drawings and predictions show how well they understand circuit diagrams. This sheet may be useful for assessment purposes. Answers - **1.** The bulb will not light when the switch is on as this causes a short circuit. Switching it off allows the bulb to light. **2.** Neither bulb will light. **3.** Bulb **a** will light but bulb **b** will not. (See page 31 for drawings of circuits.) Ask children to show their circuit drawings as diagrams.

SIA - Teachers' Resource Book 3. F2616

Electrical connections

Ask the children to think about any lights in their homes which are controlled by two different switches. Where are these mainly found (e.g. hallways, landings)? Why are they in these locations? Can the children plan and draw a circuit which will work like this? (Use one light bulb only.) Ask them to try it.

The children's first attempt at making a **two way** switch is likely to be similar to this:

1.

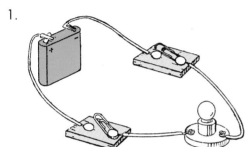

Some of their attempts may produce short circuits:

2.

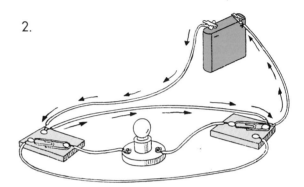

Allow them to try it. They will find, of course, that when one switch is in the 'off' position, the other will not switch on the light. This is because there is a break in the circuit.

3.

Some children may work out how to make a circuit which allows two switches to control one bulb. Most children will need help. Illustration 3 shows how to connect two circuits so that either switch may be used to switch the light on or off.

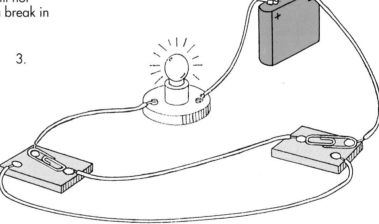

Circuit diagrams

Before introducing conventional symbols, ask the children to invent their own. Can they use them to draw bird's eye views or plans of their circuits?

Ask the class to compare their symbols.

Talk about the need for standard symbols which mean the same to everyone.
The ACTIVITY SHEET on page 30 may be useful.

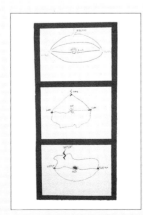

Activity sheet: Inputs and outputs

Name: _____

Your computer control interface has input (I) and output (O) ports.

- Decide which of the items in the pictures below you would connect to output and which you would connect to input.

- Draw the correct symbol in the boxes beside each picture.

a. buzzer ☐	**b.** light dependent resistor ☐	**c.** push switch ☐
d. sound sensor ☐	**e.** motor ☐	**f.** bulb ☐

- Describe (on a separate piece of paper) how each could be used with a conveyor belt.

Teachers' Notes. (Delete when photocopying.)
This sheet can be used to assess the children's understanding of an interface and how it is used. Answers - **a**:0, **b**:i, **c**:i, **d**:i, **e**:0, **f**:0. Sensors are, in effect, switches. They are either hand operated or respond to given conditions.

Sensors

Push to break switch. This is a 'not switch'. (Unlike switches it is pushed to break, not connect, the circuit.)

Introduce a variety of switches and sensors. (These can be purchased individually or as part of kits.)
Ask children to replace the home-made switches in their circuits with:

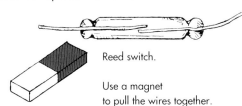

Reed switch.

Use a magnet to pull the wires together.

Light sensor (photo sensor, or light dependent resistor). Variations in light intensity cause the sensor to change the resistance in a circuit.

Compass fun

Ask the children to make a simple circuit with a switch.

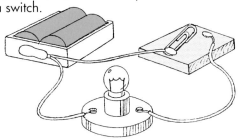

Ask them to place a compass near the circuit, as shown in picture **1**.
Switch it on and watch the compass.
The children could record their observations by drawing the circuit and describing what happens.
Can they can think of other arrangements to try (e.g. those shown in **2-4**)?

1.

2.

3.

4.

 Magnets can damage compasses. Use old compasses.

Discussion

When do the children think these sensors could be useful? They could make models of their ideas.
Suggestions include:
- a light which automatically switches on at night
- a vehicle in which the headlights are operated by the wheels (reed switch and magnet)
- a buzzer or light which is switched on when a door opens.

Introduce computer control using sensors. Can the children use this equipment to find out what happens in their classroom when they are not in it?

Hans Oersted discovered the effect of electricity on the compass. Some of the children may like to research his discovery and prepare a report for the rest of the class.

Planning and Assessment: Forces

Knowledge and Understanding of Science:
Science in everyday life.
Health and safety.

AT4 Physical Processes
iii: Forces and motion.

AT	SCIENTIFIC CONCEPT	PUPIL MATERIAL	TEACHERS' BOOK PAGE
4(iii)	Forces involved in moving through the air.		42-43
	Balance.	*Cantilever*	
	Forces in structures.	*Cantilever, Using ramps, Levers, Pulleys*	38
	How levers make work easier.	*Levers*	40-41
	How slopes make work easier.	*Using ramps*	39
	How pulleys make work easier.	*Pulleys*	
	How forces can be measured.	*Using ramps, Levers, Pulleys*	38-41
	Displacement.	*Cargoes at sea*	
	Buoyancy.	*Cargoes at sea*	

Pupil profile: Forces

Knowledge and Understanding of Science

Child's name:

Date of birth: _____   Date: _____

WHAT TO LOOK FOR	COMMENT	AT
Can recognise an aerofoil shape.		4(iii)
Understands that one way to achieve balance is to add weight to the base of a structure.		
Uses trusses to strengthen a girder bridge.		
Can position a lever so that the load is near the fulcrum and the effort is at a distance from the fulcrum.		
Knows that a wedge is a slope which helps to lift heavy objects.		
Understands that the more pulleys used, the smaller the force needed to lift an object.		
Uses a force meter to measure the force needed to lift an object (in Newtons).		
Knows that the heavier the load in a boat, the lower it floats in the water.		
Understands that objects float higher in salt water than in fresh water because salt water is denser.		

Science In Action: Forces

Teachers' Guide to the Pupil Material

Cantilever · AT4(iii)

Scientific Knowledge/Understanding
The shape of a structure affects its strength.

Background Information
The forces which are acting on the **cantilever** structure may be represented as follows:

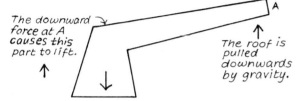

The weight of the back of the structure counters the gravitational pull (downwards) on the roof. The same principle operates in cantilever bridges.

Teacher Interaction/Organisation
The model structure is easier to make if all folds are scored. The children may find that the structure stays upright quite well, without any additional weight at the base.
The *Challenger* is an opportunity for the children to investigate what additional features are required to keep these structures standing. Plasticine may, for example, be placed in the base for extra support.

Using ramps · AT4(iii)

Scientific Knowledge/Understanding
A slope or a ramp makes it easier to lift an object.

Background Information
A slope makes a load easier to lift because it acts against gravity.
The load moves further (along the inclined plane) than it would if lifted vertically. Driving a wedge under a heavy object helps to lift it in the same way.
A screw is an inclined plane arranged in a spiral form. It is easier to turn a screw into a piece of wood than to push it in.

Teacher Interaction/Organisation
Ask the children where they have seen slopes used to help raise heavy things, e.g. wheelbarrows on building sites are often pushed up planks, small boats are pulled up slopes when taken on to the shore.
The practical activity shows how to measure forces and asks the children to compare the force required to lift the same objects:
- with/without a ramp
- with ramps of different lengths.
They should find that less force is needed when the ramp

is used. However, it is important to emphasise that we do not get something for nothing' and the object is moved over a greater distance.
The *Challenger* requires the children to make predictions based on previous experience and to test these.

Levers · AT4(iii)

Scientific Knowledge/Understanding
Levers make work easier.
A lever moves around a pivot.
Its effectiveness depends on the position of the load and where effort is applied.
A seesaw is a simple lever.
Scissors, pliers and claw hammers operate as levers.

Background Information
A simple lever operates as follows:

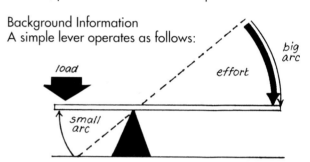

The further the effort is from the **fulcrum** (supporting block) the larger the force needed to lift the load. The closer the load is to the fulcrum the smaller the force needed to lift it.
Again the principle that we never 'get something for nothing' can be applied: the further your hand is from the fulcrum, the easier the load is to lift (i.e. the smaller the force needed to lift it) but the further your hand moves in the act of lifting.
The seesaw is a **first class lever**, because the fulcrum is between the load and the effort. All the examples shown in the introductory activity are first class levers. Second and third class levers are described on page 41.

Teacher Interaction/Organisation
The Pupil Material introduces first class levers and provides some examples of their use in everyday life.
The practical activity focuses on how to measure the effort used in lifting a mass of about 1kg with and without a lever. The effort (where the force meter is positioned) must be kept the same.

 Close supervision is needed, to ensure that children work safely and avoid the end of the pole where the weight is hanging.

Ask the children to identify the variables in this investigation:
- distance from the weight to the end of the pole
- distance from force meter to the other end of the pole weight
- the point at which the pole is balanced on the block (fulcrum).

The children should find that the nearer the weight is to the end of the pole, i.e. the further it is from the fulcrum, the larger the force will be to lift the load.

Draw their attention to the distance which their hand moves when lifting the weight. As it becomes easier to lift, the hand moves further. This demonstrates the principle that we do not 'get something for nothing'. The children could measure and record this distance.

The *Challenger* requires the children to predict, then find out, what will happen if the effort is moved progressively nearer to the fulcrum. (Remind them to control all the other variables.) They should find that the force required to lift the weight becomes progressively greater.

 Ensure that the weight cannot land on the children's feet.

Pulleys   AT4(iii)

Scientific Knowledge/Understanding
A pulley is a simple machine which makes work easier.
The more pulleys used, the less effort is required to lift a load but the hand used to operate the pulley has to move further.

Background Information
A single pulley, as shown in the introductory activity, does not reduce the force needed to lift the load. It does feel easier than a straight lift, as the hand is moving downwards, in the same direction as gravity. The load becomes progressively easier to lift as extra pulleys are added.

In ideal conditions, which are difficult to create, each pulley added should halve the original effort needed. As progressively less effort is used to lift a load, the distance through which the hand moves increases in proportion.

Teacher Interaction/Organisation
The photographs show how the practical investigation may be set up. Try to ensure that when the children lift the weight, their hands are kept in line with the pulleys. If they are moved out to one side the cord or string will slip off the pulley wheels. This activity requires the children to have the patience and persistence to keep setting up the pulleys after the cord has slipped off. Children who find this frustrating may work more effectively on other activities, e.g. *Levers*, *Using ramps*. Ensure that all of the children have an opportunity to report on or discuss their findings with the rest of the class.

Encourage the children to look for patterns in their results. The diagrams below show the arrangements of the pulleys:

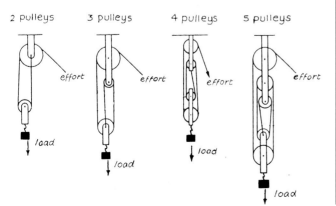

Cargoes at sea   AT4(iii)

Scientific Knowledge/Understanding
As a progressively greater load is placed in a ship or other container, it floats lower in the water. (The water level rises.) For the loading of ships, the maximum safe water level has to be worked out.

This is different in fresh/salt water and warm/cold water. This means that there have to be several markings on the ship's bow (**Plimsoll Lines**) to show maximum safe water levels for different water conditions.

Background Information
Objects float if they are less dense than water. **Archimedes' Principle** states that a body floats if it displaces its own weight in water. Materials which are not very dense, such as polystyrene and balsa wood, float very high on the water. This means they displace a small amount of water which is equal to the weight of the piece of polystyrene or balsa wood. Denser materials, such as mahogany and teak, float lower in the water, displacing more of it. Solid blocks of metal sink because they cannot displace enough water to float. (They cannot displace water of a greater weight than their own.) The children may question how a ship, which is made of metal, can float. This is because the shape of an object is also important: a piece of metal, such as a tin can, will float but once it is squashed into a small ball, it sinks. In effect the density of the whole object has been changed. A tin can, like a ship, contains a great deal of air which has a density much lower than that of water. Therefore, the object as a whole has a density which is less than water and floats. A squashed can contains little or no air and has a density higher than that of water.

Salt water is denser than fresh and cold water is denser than warm. Objects float higher in water which is more dense.

Teacher Interaction/Organisation
Provide pictures/photographs of ships, showing the Plimsoll Line. Encourage the children to use reference books to find out more about Samuel Plimsoll and Lloyd's Register. (All ships in the world have to be registered with Lloyd's of London, who have the right to inspect them at any time for their seaworthiness.)

The practical activity focuses on the relationship between the load and the water level. The children may suggest that the maximum safe load is the weight immediately lighter than the weight which made the tub sink. This could be a valuable discussion point.

- Would they be happy sailing in a ship loaded to this maximum?
- What do they think would happen if the sea became even slightly rough?

A transparent plastic aquarium tank is the ideal water container to use, as the children will be able to see the water levels clearly. The table top should be covered with an absorbent material such as an old towel.

A very small container (such as a plastic pot, tube or test tube) is recommended for the *Challenger* activity. If larger containers are used, enormous amounts of salt are required. The children can make a **saturated** solution, i.e. no more salt will dissolve in the water.

Bridges

A trussed bridge:

Collect and display pictures of various bridges and, if possible, take the children out on a bridge survey.
Ask them why they think each bridge was built.

- What does it cross?
- What does it carry?

Draw their attention to the shape and style of each bridge.

Trussed bridges

Provide pictures of trussed bridges. Can the children suggest why a truss may be used in bridge building?

The children could design and build a trussed bridge, using art straws.

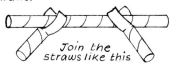

Join the straws like this

Cut open the ends of the straws

—cut

*This makes joining easier
use high quality PVA glue.*

Discussion

Compare a girder bridge with a trussed bridge. Can the children suggest where and why each should be used?
Plan an investigation to find out. Consider the length of the bridge along with the materials used.
They could place weights on or hang them from the model bridges (made from card) to find out which is the strongest.
Ask the children to experiment with placing the weights in different positions, e.g. near the centre, near the ends.

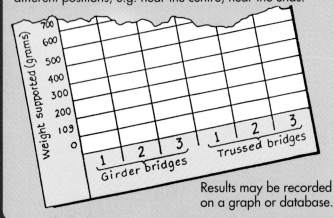

Results may be recorded on a graph or database.

Background information

The weakest point of a span is the centre. By using a number of trusses the bridge is strengthened as they help to spread out the downward force of any weight.
If the joints at **a**, **b** and **c** are strong, a weight at **c** will not only push downwards on the bridge at that point, but also pull the struts **ac** and **bc** downwards.

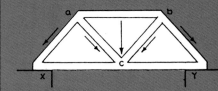

The strut **ab** is also pulled downwards. This pushes downwards on the two struts at the ends (**ax** and **by**). This means that the downward force is not all at **c**, but is spread over the whole of the bridge.

SIA - Teachers' Resource Book 3. F2616

Slopes

 Close supervision is needed.

Easy way up

Make a steep slope, using firmly anchored PE equipment. It should be as wide as possible and tested before it is used to ensure it is safe.
If the wheels of the truck do not grip, cover the slope with a large rubber or foam mat, or put elastic bands over the wheels as tyres.
Ask the children to load a small wheeled trolley or toy truck with a weight of approximately 3-5kg (e.g. a bag of sand). Check that this is safely secured.

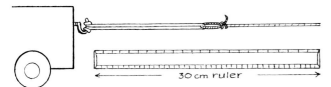

30 cm ruler

Investigate and compare the effort needed to:
-   pull the load straight up the slope
-   zig-zag the load up the slope.

One method is to attach an elastic band to the truck. Use the band to move the truck and ask a friend to measure the stretch, or use a Newton meter.

Collect and display photographs of roads which lead up steep hills.
Can the children explain why these roads tend to be a zig-zag or spiral shape?

Provide a cone shape to represent a steep sided mountain.
Ask the children how they would design a road to go up it.
The road could be made with a thin strip of paper.

They should consider the steepness of the slope.

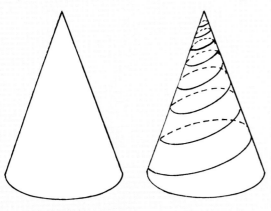

A screw is a spiral slope.

Spiral slopes

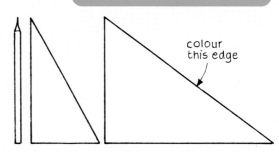

colour this edge

Ask the children to make some slopes which are the same height as a pencil. They should measure the height of the slope, and when they wrap it round the pencil, count the number of turns.

This should enable them to work out the number of turns per centimetre, or the pitch of the screw.

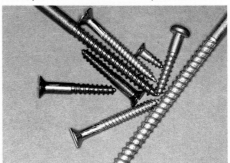

Using levers

Provide a strong brush handle or other smooth piece of wood and ask the children to try carrying a bag of sand suspended from it.
They should rest it on one shoulder.

 Ensure that other children keep clear. Ask one child in each group to watch the suspended bag at all times.

In which position do the children find it easiest to carry:
- longest part in front of their shoulder
- longest part behind their shoulder?

Can the children measure the force needed to keep the pole level in different positions? A force meter may be useful for this.

Remind the children about fair testing. Try to control any variables, such as the position of the force meter on the pole.

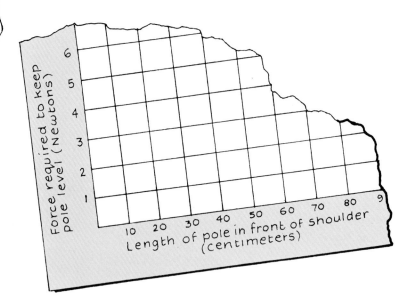

Discussion

Force meters are spring balances calibrated in Newtons. A force of 10 Newtons (10N) is roughly equal to 1kg in weight.

Background information
The pole acts as a lever, whose pivot (or fulcrum) is the shoulder.

This is a first class lever, as the effort and load are on opposite sides of the fulcrum:

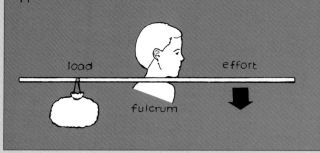

Provide a selection of force meters, with different scales, from which the children can select the most suitable.
A force meter designed to measure large forces, e.g. 0-10N, has a stronger spring than one designed to measure smaller forces, e.g. 0-2.5N.

Wheelbarrows

Does a wheelbarrow reduce the force needed to lift a load, or does it just make it feel easier to lift?
Ask the children to plan a fair investigation to find out. They could lift a small bag of sand or compost with/ without a wheelbarrow and measure the forces using a meter.

Suggest that they try this using bags of compost (or sand) of different weights.

Findings could be recorded on a graph.

Force needed to lift a wheelbarrow (Newtons)			
weight	Left hand	Right hand	Total
1 kg			
2 kg			
3 kg			
4 kg			

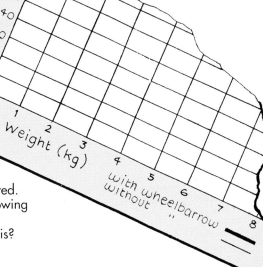

It may also be useful to find the force needed to lift the empty wheelbarrow.

Ask the children to draw the wheelbarrow and compost being lifted. This could be a diagram which labels the load and an arrow showing the direction in which it is pushing.
Can they also label where the effort used to lift the wheelbarrow is?
See if the children can also identify the fulcrum or pivot.

Discussion

Background information
The wheelbarrow acts as a lever whose load and effort are on the same side of the fulcrum.
This is a second class lever.
When the load and effort are also on the same side of the fulcrum but the effort is between the load and the fulcrum it is known as a third class lever.

Do not allow children to overstrain themselves.

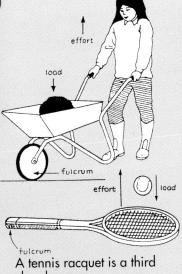

A tennis racquet is a third class lever.

Aerofoils

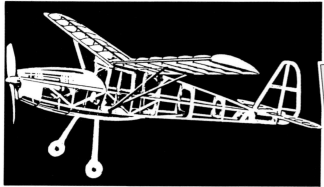

If possible visit an airport, air force base or transport museum.
Collect and display photographs and models of aircraft. Talk about the shape of the aircraft, drawing the children's attention to the shape of the wings in cross-section.
Provide shapes for comparison:

back   front   Tick the box by the shape of an aircraft wing section

Make a model glider with aerofoils. A kit from a model shop may provide the best example.
Ask the children to compare it with a model with no aerofoils
Look at aerofoils on racing cars. Draw their attention to the fact that the aerofoil shape on a racing car is the opposite way up to the shape of an aeroplane's wings.
The rear of a fast-moving, streamlined car has a tendency to lift off the ground. The aerofoil keeps the car close to the ground.

Aerofoil shapes

The children could make and test aerofoil shapes. Two possible methods are:

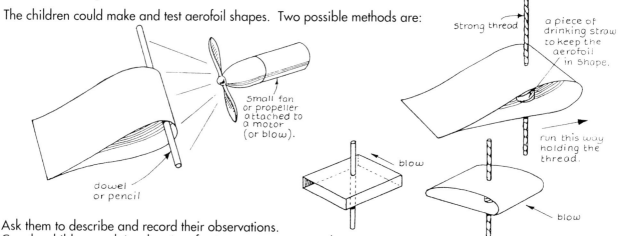

Small fan or propeller attached to a motor (or blow).

dowel or pencil

Strong thread

a piece of drinking straw to keep the aerofoil in shape.

run this way holding the thread.

blow

blow

Ask them to describe and record their observations.
Can the children explain why aircraft wings are not rectangular in cross-section?

Lift

An aerofoil causes air to move quickly over the top of an aircraft's wing. This aerofoil helps the craft to lift. Aerofoils on cars are upside-down to prevent lift. Birds' wings have aerofoil shapes. The shape made by a flying kite is also an aerofoil, which is why it lifts.

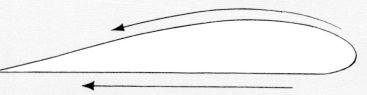

air moves more quickly over the top.

air moves more slowly here.

The slowly-moving air exerts greater pressure, pushing upwards, so the wing lifts.

Kites

Collect and display a variety of commercially produced kites, along with any reference material.
Try flying some of these with the children.

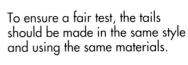

 Never fly kites near overhead electrical wires.

Which kites do the children find easiest to fly?
Can they suggest why some fly better than others?

Ask the children to investigate the difference made by having a tail on a kite. They could experiment with:
- no tail
- tail the same length as the kite
- tail twice the length of the kite, etc.

The ideal length is 5 times the length of the kite.

To ensure a fair test, the tails should be made in the same style and using the same materials.

Design different kinds of tails.

Pictures of Chinese kites may provide ideas. Try them out.

Flying kites

Ideally, a large open space away from traffic or airports should be used, They can, however, be tested on a small school field and playground with care, although the children may not be able to keep them flying for any length of time.
Ideal wind conditions are between Beaufort Scale 2 and 4.
Launch a kite by **winching**, instead of by running.

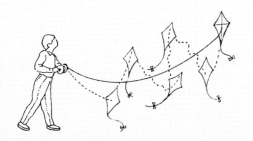

Planning and Assessment: Materials

Knowledge and Understanding of Science:
Science in everyday life.
Health and safety.

AT2 Life and Living Processes
  i: Life processes.
AT3 Materials and their Properties
  i: Grouping and classifying materials.
  iii: Changing materials.

AT4 Physical Processes
  ii: Energy.
  iii: Forces and motion.

AT	SCIENTIFIC CONCEPT	PUPIL MATERIAL	TEACHERS' BOOK PAGE
2(i)	Humans (and other living things) need food for growth.		53
3(i)	Uses of flexible materials.	*Tied up* *Sports shoes*	50-51
	Elasticity and its uses.		52
	Adhesion: joining materials by chemical means.	*Sticky business*	49
	Joining materials by mechanical means.	*Tied up*	48-52
	Characteristics of wood.		48
	Capillary action: how water behaves in tubes and narrow spaces.	*Tubes*	51
	Dangers of everyday materials.	Should be stressed at all times.	
3(iii)	Chemical changes.	*Reactions*	53
	Rusting.		49
4(ii)	Food as an energy source.		53
4(iii)	Friction.	*Sports shoes*	

Pupil profile: Materials

Knowledge and Understanding of Science

Child's name: _____

Date of birth: _____   Date: _____

WHAT TO LOOK FOR	COMMENT	AT
Knows that some foods are particularly important for growth.		2(i)
Understands that sports shoes need to be flexible to provide mobility.		3(i)
Knows that some fibres stretch more than others.		
Understands that certain adhesives will only glue particular materials. Selects a suitable glue for joining wood to wood.		
Understands that nails join wood in the same way that drawing pins and staples join paper.		
Understands that oval nails (placed along the grain of a piece of wood) are less likely to split it than round nails.		
Knows that water rises up narrow spaces.		
Knows that iodine is poisonous.		
Knows that iodine turns blue/black when in contact with starch.		3(iii)
Understands that iron and steel rust when in contact with air and water.		
Knows that fat (oil) can be burned.		4(ii)
Understands that friction can provide grip which can be useful to start movement.		4(iii)

Science In Action: Materials

Teachers' Guide to the Pupil Material

Tied up — AT3(i)

Scientific Knowledge/Understanding
Materials have different properties which make them suitable for different purposes.
To be tied or knotted, materials need to be flexible.

Teacher Interaction/Organisation
The introductory activity focuses on three common types of knots. The instructions for tying these knots illustrate the ends of the strings only. The children will require two pieces of string for both the **granny** and **reef** knots.
Ask the children to investigate which of these knots join the strings together and which let the string slip.
Encourage them to look for knots used for everyday purposes. Can the children suggest another knot which may be more suitable for the purpose?
The practical activity takes a closer look at the materials themselves. Ensure that the same knot is used to join each pair of materials. Ask the children to explain why each pair of materials should/should not be joined by a knot. Try testing each pair with another type of knot to find out whether this variable makes any difference.

Sports shoes — AT3(i) 4(iii)

Scientific Knowledge/Understanding
Properties of materials which are important in the manufacture of sports shoes include:
- flexibility
- weight
- ability to create friction.

Friction provides grip on a surface to make movement begin, stop or change direction.

Background Information
Friction is a force which tries to stop one surface sliding over another. In some situations friction is a hindrance: e.g. on a slide, in a machine. It is reduced by such actions as polishing and oiling. To start to walk or run, the foot has to push against the ground. With less friction, e.g. when wearing slippery shoes, the necessary grip is difficult to achieve.

Teacher Interaction/Organisation
A collection of shoes for different purposes, or of shoe catalogues could be a good starting point for this activity. Include shoes for as many different sport and leisure activities as possible, e.g. aerobics, gymnastics, long distance running, general fitness training, ballet, squash, riding.
Ask the children to note how the shoes are similar and how they are different. Many shoes for long distance running have the back part cut away so that it does not rub against the Achilles tendon. Some have special grip, e.g. spikes for running on grass. Why do the children think football boots with studs are unsuitable for wear on a hard surface, such as the playground? Important features for the shoes illustrated are:

1. (d) Football boots have studs to provide extra grip on grass surfaces.
2. (c) Tennis shoes need to provide grip for both grass and hard surfaces. They are different from training shoes in the way the sole is attached. (It is often moulded over part of the upper, to provide support.) This helps to prevent the foot slipping over sideways, damaging the wearer's ankles. The children may also be familiar with the shoes worn for aerobics. These are also designed to help avoid such injuries but are lighter in weight and less hardwearing than tennis shoes.
3. (b) Golf shoes, like football boots, provide grip on grass surfaces. They are shaped to be comfortable for walking rather than running.
4. (a) Cycling shoes need to be slipped easily in and out of foot restraints on the pedals. They do not need hardwearing soles, as they rarely touch the ground. The soles are very hard and stiff so that the pedals do not cause discomfort. Pedals can be fastened to the shoes. They do not need to grip.

This work could be effectively linked to learning about the body and how to keep fit and healthy while avoiding injury. Look for safety features of sports shoes and talk about why they should not be worn for inappropriate activities. The practical investigation focuses on testing the flexibility of materials. Encourage the children to consider all the variables before they begin and to check that these are controlled.
The *Challenger* involves the children in an investigation to compare the grip of different soles. Everyday shoes could be compared with sports shoes. Each shoe should be tested on the selected surfaces and the results recorded. One method is to pull them along each surface using a force meter. The investigation will provide more realistic results if a weight is placed in each shoe tested. (Ensure it is the same weight to make it a fair test.) A 5kg weight is recommended for this investigation. Weights are available from educational suppliers.

 Handle weights with care. They should be enclosed in strong card, with a handle attached which cannot become loose.

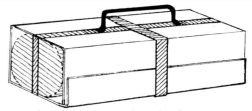

Encourage the children to select the force meter with an appropriate scale.

Tubes   AT3(i) 4(iii)

Scientific Knowledge/Understanding
Liquids (and gases) can travel along the inside of the tubes; solids cannot. Water has an invisible 'skin' which pulls its surface into a curved shape.

In most containers which are filled to the brim this can be seen as a convex curve:

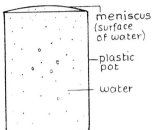

meniscus (surface of water)

plastic pot

water

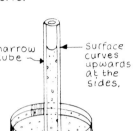

narrow tube — surface curves upwards at the sides.

When a container is partially filled, the edges of the water's surface are pulled upwards, making a concave curve (best seen in narrow containers).

This makes water rise up tubes, and in fabrics to rise up the spaces between fibres.

Background Information
The tendency of water to rise up narrow spaces is called capillary action. Plants take up water by capillary action.

Teacher Interaction/Organisation
The introductory activity draws the children's attention to the everyday applications of tubes. It could also be used to assess their ideas about materials which can/cannot pass through different tubes.
The practical activity requires the children to observe closely how water behaves in tubes of different widths. Ask them to note any patterns in their observations. They should find that the narrower the tube, the higher the water rises. Encourage the children to identify all the variables involved, noting which one is changed and which are kept the same, e.g. time.
Use the *Challenger* to draw the children's attention to the spaces, or 'holes', between the fibres in each fabric. Provide hand lenses or, if possible, a binocular microscope.

Sticky business   AT3(i) 4(iii)

Scientific Knowledge/Understanding
A useful property of some materials is their ability to stick (adhere) to others.
Different adhesives are suitable for different purposes.

Background Information
Adhesive substances bond two surfaces together. In order to adhere, the adhesive's molecules have to form a bond with the molecules of both surfaces.

Teacher Interaction/Organisation
Provide a collection of sticky tapes, and ask the children to bring in their own samples. This is safer than using glues, since they may bring unsuitable samples (solvent based).

When testing the tapes in the practical investigation, encourage the children to notice which surface the tape comes away from each time. The findings of the *Challenger* could be recorded on a chart of the following type:

What did the tape remain stuck to?			
	paper	plastic	metal
paper			
plastic			
metal			

Reactions   AT3(i) (iii)

Scientific Knowledge/Understanding
Materials can be combined to form new materials.
Some changes are irreversible.
Certain combinations of materials cause chemical reactions, such as fizzing (effervescence) which is useful for baking and in the manufacture of carbonated drinks.

Background Information
When a liquid acid is mixed with a carbonate, carbon dioxide is released. The release of the gas causes the effervescence. Bicarbonate of soda, limestone, chalk and marble are all carbonates. When bicarbonate of soda is mixed with water no carbon dioxide is produced because there is no acid present. The reaction with acid is important in cooking when the acid comes from another source, e.g. lemon juice or vinegar. Baking powder does contain an acid and so will fizz in water. This is more noticeable when the water is warm.

Teacher Interaction/Organisation
The introductory activity focuses on the reaction between acids and carbonates. It may also be used to assess the children's understanding. The answers are: **2, 3, 4, 5** and **6** will fizz as acid is present but **1** will not.
Provide tubs of baking powder and bicarbonate of soda for the children to compare their ingredients. Can they suggest which ingredient causes the reaction?
The practical activity is an opportunity for the children to check their predictions and to explain what they notice. Instructions for testing for acidity can be found on page 49, *Teachers' Resource Book 2*.
Effervescing containers of baking powder mixtures can be messy. Stand them in a shallow tray, and provide cloths for mopping up.
The *Challenger* requires close supervision only when the biscuits are cooked. Encourage the children to collect the equipment themselves and to organise their work (including the washing up). Provide a selection of books which give biscuit recipes. These should not list baking powder in the ingredients, since biscuits are not intended to rise.
Before starting, the table tops should be covered with plastic sheeting which has been cleaned and wiped with a safe sterilising liquid. Useful materials to have available include: an oven, scales, timer, mixing bowl, baking trays, biscuit cutters, forks, spoons, table knife, rolling pins and a selection of ingredients.

Joining wood

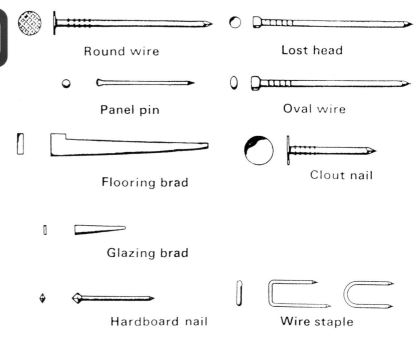

Round wire

Lost head

Masonry nail

Panel pin

Oval wire

Upholstery nail

Flooring brad

Clout nail

Glazing brad

Hardboard nail

Wire staple

Collect, label and display a variety of nails. Ask the children to draw them from the side and also from the top to show the shape of the head. What similarities and differences do they notice?

Draw their attention to:
- the shape and size of the head
- shape in cross-section
- thickness
- size
- whether or not the nail is galvanised (coated with a thin layer of zinc, to prevent rusting).

Ask the children to suggest what makes each nail suitable for a particular purpose.

Safe fingers

Can the children think of a way to hold a nail to help them avoid hitting their fingers when hammering it in?

Encourage the children to use several fairly light taps, rather than heavy blows.
They should hold the end of the handle.

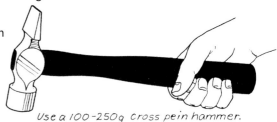

Use a 100 - 250g cross pein hammer.

Ensure that hammer heads are not loose. Close supervision is needed.

Oval or round?

Show the children how to safely knock nails into wood. Use an offcut from a plank or floorboard. Try masonry nails, round wire, and oval wire nails. Ask the children to compare oval nails with the long axis **with**, and **against** the grain:

Look for splits in the wood. Watch what happens when several nails are driven into wood in a line with the grain:

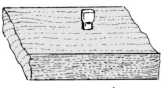

with the grain

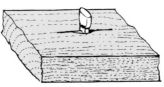

against the grain

How do the children think this can be prevented?

Glues

Do the children think it matters what kind of glue is used for joining wood to wood? Ask them to plan a fair test to find out. The ACTIVITY SHEET: *Planning sheet* may be useful (page 20).

 Do not use solvent based glues. If a glue gun is used, the 'low melt' kind is safer than a very hot one. Close supervision is needed.

Encourage the children to control variables: the type and size of wood used, the surface glued, the amount of overlap. If the overlap is kept small (1-2cm) it should not require great force to separate it.

 Check your Local Authority health and safety guidelines.

Use wood which will not easily snap.

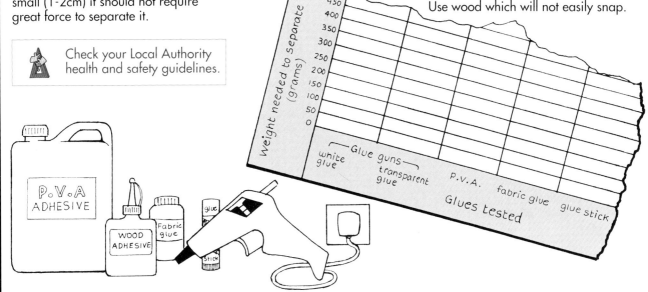

Discussion

Which nails do the children think will rust? Ask them to find out. Can they tell what kind of metal they are made from? *Teachers' Resource Book 1*, page 27, provides an introduction to metal testing. See also *Teachers' Resource Book 4*, pages 52-53.

Background information
Most nails are made of steel or iron. Those intended for outdoor use are often galvanised (coated with zinc which does not rust) or made of brass. The heads of some nails are designed to sink into wood for easy disguising: e.g. lost head, hard board pin. A nail punch may be used to drive them further into the wood.

Ask them to test the strength of glued joints between pieces of 10mm square section wood; some with one or two card triangles.

Activity sheet: Knots

Name: _____

- Tick when you can tie each knot.
- Keep a sample of each knot to make a display.

1. overhand ☐	2. figure of eight ☐	3. reef ☐
4. clove hitch ☐	5. surgeon's ☐	6. sheet bend ☐
7. quick release ☐	8. fisherman's ☐	9. bowline ☐
10. running bowline ☐	11. carrick bend ☐	12. round turn and two half hitches ☐

Teachers' Notes. (Delete when photocopying.)
Ask the children to notice if the knot 'slips' (moves along the string/allows the string to move through it). Encourage them to think of places where each knot may be suitable. Information from sailing and other outdoor activity organisations may be useful.

Rope and string

Collect a variety of ropes and strings.
Suggest to the children that they look at them through a powerful magnifying glass.
What do they think each type is made of?
Ask them to separate and count the fibres.

Joining poles with string

Makeshift tent frames made from garden canes may be lashed together with string. Allow the children to try their own ideas, and then show them some knots. See if they can design and make more complex frames, and test their stability.

Strings and wicks

Ask the children which strings they think will soak up water.
Which will absorb it most quickly?
Include candle wicks (which can be bought from candle makers) and, if possible, wicks used in oil lamps and heaters.
Encourage the children to plan their own investigation.

They could use ACTIVITY SHEET:
Planning sheet, page 20.

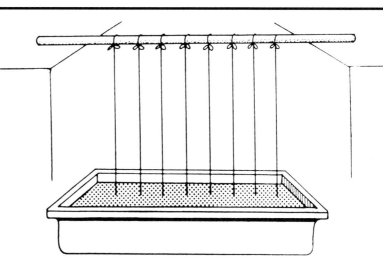

What do the children think would happen if they left very long pieces of string with their ends in water?
Is there a limit to how far the water will soak?
Plan an investigation to find out.

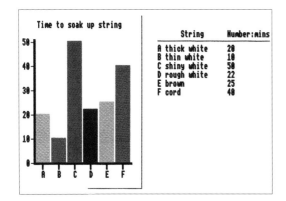

Time to soak up string

String	Number:mins
A thick white	20
B thin white	10
C shiny white	50
D rough white	22
E brown	25
F cord	40

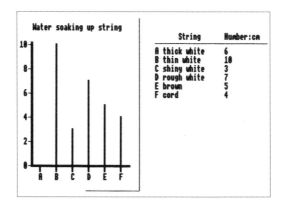

Water soaking up string

String	Number:cm
A thick white	6
B thin white	10
C shiny white	3
D rough white	7
E brown	5
F cord	4

Fibres and fabrics

Ask the children to compare sports clothes with clothes for more formal occasions. Useful items for comparison include tracksuits, T shirts, sweatshirts, sports vests, school shirts, trousers, jackets.

Can they explain what makes some clothes more comfortable for sports than others?

Draw the children's attention to stretch, closeness of fit, comfort, etc.

Does it stretch?

Sports clothing is often made from stretchy material.

Ask the children to find out which clothes are made from stretchy fabrics.

Draw their attention to the direction of stretch: horizontal, vertical or diagonal. Focus on the fabric itself, asking them to look at the direction of the weave.

If possible provide a garment where the fabric is **bias cut**, for comparison.

bias cut

straight cut

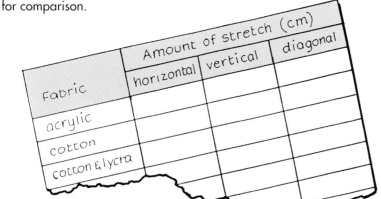

Fabric	Amount of stretch (cm)		
	horizontal	vertical	diagonal
acrylic			
cotton			
cotton & lycra			

Finding the stretchiest fabric

Children can measure similar-sized pieces of material, before and after they have stretched them.

Did they notice which fabrics returned to their original size? Look at and feel the direction of the nap to find which is horizontal, which vertical.

Discussion

The nap of this fabric runs in this direction:

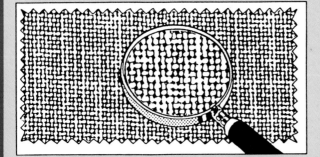

Vertical means with the nap and horizontal means across it.

Can the children think what makes the fabric stretch diagonally but not necessarily horizontally or vertically?

Background information

Fabrics stretch vertically if the threads running in that direction have elasticity (stretch). If different fibres are used horizontally, the fabric may not stretch in this direction, and vice versa. Most fabrics will stretch more **diagonally** than horizontally or vertically, because it may not be the threads themselves which stretch. They move about, sliding on each other. Find the direction of a fabric's nap by running your fingers across it in different directions. If your fingers move against the nap, tiny fibres are raised leaving a slightly darker, shadowy mark on the fabric.

Food for thought

Food is needed in order to grow, as well as for energy to move and keep warm.

What do the children think 'growing' really means?
Explain that our food becomes part of us (i.e. converted into new cells). The foods contain protein which helps the body to grow and to repair itself.

Can the children suggest why adults, who have stopped growing, also need protein?
(Protein is required to replace the cells which are continually dying and for repair.)

Pupil Book 4, pages 30-31, considers food for energy. See also *Teachers' Resource Book 4*, pages 54-64, *Our Bodies*.

Ask the children to make a 'Food for Growth' collage, showing foods containing protein.

What is food made of?

Introduce the idea of testing food to find out what it contains. Which foods do the children think contain starch? (They may have heard of foods described as starchy.)

A few small drops of iodine solution should be added to each food. If starch is present, the iodine turns blue/black. Iodine is poisonous.

 Do not allow tasting. Iodine is poisonous.

Food	Prediction	Colour of iodine	Contains starch
bread	starch	blue/black	✓
rice	no starch	blue/black	✓
apple	no starch	yellow	✗
milk	no starch	yellow	✗
biscuit	starch	blue/black	✓

Background information
The body can change starch into sugars which provide energy. Energy is stored as fat, which can then be used by the body when energy is needed.

Acid and alkali

Show the children how to test for acid in foods using litmus paper.

If blue litmus paper turns red, there is acid in the food.
If blue litmus stays blue, the food is alkaline **or** neutral.
If red litmus turns blue, the food is alkaline.

Food	Colour of litmus	Acid or alkaline
lemon	red	acid
vinegar	red	acid

Can the children predict what will happen to the acid foods if they add acid indigestion cures? Ask them to plan a fair test to find out whether they are effective.

 Very close supervision is needed. Warn children never to take medicines unless given by an adult.

Planning and Assessment: Animal Life

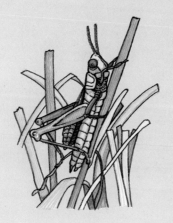

Knowledge and Understanding of Science:
Science in everyday life.
Health and safety.

AT2 Life and Living Processes
i: Life processes.
iv: Variation and classification.
v: Living things in their environment.

AT	SCIENTIFIC CONCEPT	PUPIL MATERIAL	TEACHERS' BOOK PAGE
2(i)	How animals feed.	*Beaks*	58
	How animals move.	*Birdwatch* *Birds' feet*	
	Animals' behaviour.	*Birdwatch*	59, 61-63
	Animal reproduction.	*Survivors*	
	The role of microbes in food production and decay.	*Micro organisms*	
2(iv)	Similarities and differences between animals.	*Birdwatch , Birds' feet,* *Beaks, Survivors*	60, 63-64
	Identification of locally occurring animals.	*Birdwatch*	59
	Using keys for classification.		63, 64
2(v)	How animals are suited to their habitats.	*Birds' feet*	60, 61, 63
	Competition between animals for resources.	*Beaks* *Survivors*	58
	How seasonal change affects animals.		61, 63
	How daily change affects animals.		63
	Food chains.		62

Pupil profile: Animal Life

Knowledge and Understanding of Science

Child's name:

Date of birth: _____ Date: _____

WHAT TO LOOK FOR	COMMENT	AT
Knows that the shape of a bird's beak is suited to its method of feeding, e.g. a pelican can scoop up many small fish.		2(i)
Understands that webbed feet help a water bird to paddle.		
Understands that some birds fly in flocks to make it difficult for predators to isolate individuals.		
Knows that most mammals give birth to live young. Names some animals which lay eggs.		
Knows that microbes are useful in making yogurt.		
Names and describes some animals which use camouflage to protect themselves. Describes how they are different from each other.		2(iv)
Identifies three or four local birds according to beak and foot shapes and sizes.		
Uses a key to classify birds according to beak and foot shapes.		
Knows why certain birds live near rivers.		2(v)
Knows that many birds compete for the same foods.		
Names some animals which hibernate in winter and some which migrate.		
Records the presence of various types of bird, noting which are seen in particular weather conditions.		
Knows that snails may not survive in the wild because thrushes eat them. Know that snails eat plants.		

Science In Action: Animal Life

Teachers' Guide to the Pupil Material

Birdwatch   AT2(i) (v)

Scientific Knowledge/Understanding
Birds behave in particular ways when feeding, breeding and travelling.
This behaviour allows them to maintain an awareness of their surroundings in order to protect themselves from predators.
Different species of bird have characteristic ways of moving.

Teacher Interaction/Organisation
The introductory activity shows a practical observation which could be carried out from a suitable classroom window.
Provide reference material for the practical investigation to help the children recognise local bird species. A visit from a representative of an organisation which promotes the conservation and care of birds could be very useful.
The children may find it difficult to identify species precisely. Encourage them to notice their overall shape and how they move. This information can be used to group the birds and may help the children to identify them by name.
The results of the children's investigation for the *Challenger* will be different depending on which birds are observed. Swifts, for example, spend most of their time flying. Starlings spend most of their time feeding on the discarded food near buildings or gleaning grasslands.
Remind the children that they need to keep very quiet so they will not frighten away any birds. Can they think of a way to watch the birds without being seen by them?

Birds' feet   AT2(i) (iv) (v)

Scientific Knowledge/Understanding
Birds nest and feed in places which are suited to their bodily structures:
- webbed feet are suitable for swimming
- small claws are suitable for perching on branches, as well as small jutting cliff ledges, walls, fences, etc.
- large claws can grip not only large areas of rock but also grasp small animals and birds.

The answers to the introductory activity are: **1, 3** and **5** are water birds.

Background Information
Birds' feet can be classified as follows:
- not webbed, e.g. pied wagtail, sky lark, starling
- webbed, e.g. herring gull, common tern, black headed gull.

 starling    herring gull

Teacher Interaction/Organisation
The introductory activity focuses on webbed and non-webbed feet. Children who are interested in birds, and already have more detailed knowledge, may like to find pictures which they can classify by more detailed descriptions of their feet.
The practical activity provides an opportunity for children to find out what difference webbed feet make in water. Do any of the children use flippers to swim? What difference do they make? Can they explain why they make this difference? (Flippers provide a greater surface area. This allows the swimmer to move greater amounts of water in the opposite direction and propels the wearer forwards.)
The *Challenger* investigates the claws of birds of prey. These are efficient for grasping rather than perching. Some birds of prey are also able to hold slippery creatures such as fish in their claws.

Beaks   AT2(i) (iv)

Scientific Knowledge/Understanding
Birds' beaks are a suitable shape for their particular feeding habits.

Background Information
Birds are vertebrates, and are divided into families. One way in which particular bird families can be recognised is by the shape of their beaks:

Teacher Interaction/Organisation
The introductory activity draws the children's attention to the differences between birds' feet. If possible provide pet birds so their beaks can be observed in more detail. Budgerigars and canaries, for example, have small curved beaks suitable for pecking at seeds.
Answers to the introductory activity:
1. c. The blackbird's beak can grasp and pull a worm from the ground.
2. a. The kingfisher's long, slightly curved beak is used to grasp fish as they swim.
3. b. The owl's sharp beak can tear the flesh from small animals.

Use reference material (including videos) which show the birds feeding. These can also be used to introduce them to birds which they have not seen locally.

Encourage the children to observe birds feeding in their local environment. This can be done by setting up a bird table which can be seen from the classroom window.

Do the children notice which birds eat scattered small pieces of food, which birds eat hanging foods (such as peanuts in nets) and which take and tear up large pieces of food?

Can the children use reference books to find out which birds are carnivores and which are herbivores? Can they draw food chains to show what is eaten by, and what eats various birds?

Demonstrate to the children the conventional method for representing food chains:

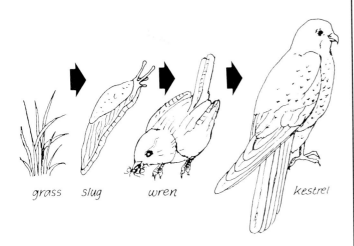

grass   slug   wren   kestrel

The arrows in a food chain always point from plant to animal. The order is determined by which plant/animal is prey to another, e.g.

plant $\longrightarrow$ herbivore $\longrightarrow$ carnivore.

Survivors   AT2(i) (iv)

Scientific Knowledge/Understanding
Some animals, including birds, reptiles, fish and insects, lay eggs.

Most mammals give birth to live young.

Some egg-laying animals lay a small number of eggs, which they guard carefully.

Others lay many in a safe place and do not stay to look after them.

Sometimes only a few out of many eggs survive.

Eggs laid in captivity are more likely to hatch as they are protected from predators and are provided with ideal warmth, light and moisture conditions.

Teacher Interaction/Organisation
The information from the introductory activity could be used to produce a large classroom display. This could classify the animals into egg-laying and non egg-laying groups. The first group could then be further divided into smaller groups, e.g. reptiles, birds, fish and arthropods.

The practical activity is most successfully carried out in late spring/early summer, as this is when snails breed. Snails have been chosen for this activity as they can be kept in plant propagators or aquariums in the classroom for long periods without causing them any harm. Look for eggs buried in soil and under stones.

Keep the habitat moist by spraying it with water, and clean by removing droppings. (A spatula should be used for this.) Collect leaves from the area in which the snails were found. These can be fed to them. Alternatively they will eat lettuce, cucumber, cabbage and apple. A supply of calcium is essential to keep the shells healthy. Pieces of limestone or chalk should be placed in the habitat (do not use blackboard chalk, which may contain harmful chemicals) along with a mixture of dried milk, calcium carbonate powder, oatmeal and water, mixed to a porridge-like consistency.

The practical activity should show how many of the eggs laid are healthy as none will be eaten by predators. The *Challenger* compares this with the survival rate of eggs in their natural environment.

Micro organisms   AT4(i) (iv)

Scientific Knowledge/Understanding
Micro organisms are tiny living things, too small to be seen without a powerful microscope.

Some can harm us, as they cause diseases.

Some breed in dirt and waste, causing unpleasant smells. This is why we need to keep ourselves and food areas clean. Others are useful, e.g. in food production.

Background Information
Any food preparation process involving fermentation makes use of the action of micro organisms, e.g. beer, cheese, wines, spirits, yogurt, vinegar, tofu, coffee, tea, among others. The organisms secrete enzymes which change the flavour and appearance of the food. *Quorn* is a myco protein made from micro organisms growing on food industry waste products.

Teacher Interaction/Organisation
Use the introductory activity to introduce the word **micro organism** to the children. They include viruses and bacteria. The picture focuses on bacteria which can be useful.

This may also provide an opportunity to talk with the children about bacteria which multiply in places where there is dirt and cause unpleasant smells. (*Teachers' Resource Book 4, Micro organisms and people*, page 64, covers the need to keep clean in order to smell pleasant and minimise disease and infection.)

Provide samples of foods shown in the picture, if possible. If they are to be tasted, ensure that conditions are hygenic. The practical activity explains how to make yogurt.

 Since milk needs to be heated, close supervision is needed.

It is advised that an adult pours out the boiling milk and adds an equal quantity of cold milk. The children will then be able to handle it with safety.

'Live' yogurt must be used as this has living bacteria. These multiply in warm conditions.

If the milk is too hot the bacteria will be destroyed.

Hunting and foraging

Provide a variety of small animals for the children to observe feeding. These could be children's pets, or others borrowed for a day, e.g. gerbil, snail, hamster, canary, guinea pig, rabbit. (Check Local Education Authority health and safety guidelines.)

Hamsters

Can the children think why hamsters fill their cheek pouches with food and take it back to their nests to eat?
How would this way of eating be useful in the wild? (The food is stored for later use.)

How much does it eat?

Ask the children to plan fair tests to find out how much various animals eat.
They should observe what has happened to food which has gone from where it was placed. Has the animal stored it for later use?

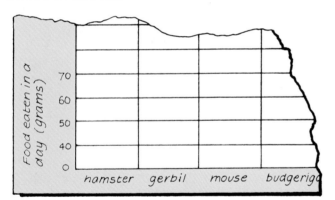

Background information
Hamsters and many other herbivores spend most of their time eating in order to provide themselves with enough energy. If they can eat in the safety of their nests they are less likely to be eaten themselves.

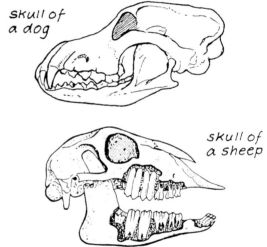

skull of a dog

skull of a sheep

Teeth and food

Show videos of carnivores and omnivores eating. Discuss pets' eating habits.
Do the children notice any differences and similarities in how they eat? Which chew and which tear their food?
Compare the teeth of animals. Use reference material or visit a museum to look at animal skulls.

Owls

Owls eat entire small animals such as mice, and smaller birds, including fur, feathers and bones.
They regurgitate the parts which they cannot digest, in the form of pellets.

 Plastic gloves should be worn while examining owl pellets (best dissected in water) to find out what has been eaten.

Flocks and herds

Ask the children to think of animals which are seen in large groups.
Watch insects and other small creatures.
Watch birds.
Pictures, slides and videos are useful for studying larger animals and those of other countries.

Safety in numbers

Ask the children to predict:

● Would a sparrowhawk have more chance of catching a sparrow if it chases one, or a flock of sparrows?

Play *Sparrows and sparrowhawk.*

The children stand in a circle and throw a **sparrow** (any small soft toy, or bean bag).

The **sparrowhawk** stands in the centre and tries to catch the **sparrow**.

More **sparrows** are introduced and thrown across the circle from one child to another.

Discussion

Which did the children find easier to catch, when playing *Sparrows and sparrowhawk:*

● a solitary sparrow
● one of a flock?

Can they think of other animals which fly in groups for protection against predators?

Animals which live in groups

Set up a formicarium, to study ants.
Look for ants helping each other to move things.
Keep the formicarium covered with thick, dark paper, unless it is being observed. This encourages ants to dig near the edges of the glass where they can be seen.

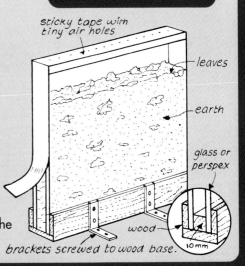

sticky tape with tiny air holes

leaves

earth

glass or perspex

wood

10mm

brackets screwed to wood base.

Arrow
poison frog

Surviving

Animals which can be kept in school, found in the local environment, or are kept as pets are an effective starting point.
If possible visit a zoo, natural history museum or aquarium.
Show videos and display pictures.
Ask the children to consider how each animal avoids being eaten. They might:
- move very quickly, kick, scratch, bite
- look frightening or be camouflaged
- have thick skin or a shell
- produce a foul smell, or be foul-tasting, etc.
(See also the ACTIVITY SHEET: *Don't eat me*, page 62.)

Kingfisher

Animal Defences				
shell	foul smell	prickles	moving quickly	burrow
snail	bombardier beetle	hedgehog	cat	mole
crab	skunk	porcupine		

Seven spot
ladybird

How do the children think animals know which other animals are poisonous or foul-tasting before they eat them? Collect and display pictures of them, look at books and videos.

Most poisonous and foul-tasting animals are very brightly coloured. Ask the children to find as many as they can, using secondary sources. Can they discover any exceptions?

Discussion

Would you eat it?

Are we ever put off food by its colour?

Use food dyes from vegetable colours to give foods unusual colours.

> Ensure that children wash their hands and all utensils are clean.

Bread, instant mashed potato and cornflour are easily coloured.
Ask the children to test their friends:
- with blindfolds
- without blindfolds.

Do they like the foods sampled in both tests?
Can the children explain this?

Surviving winter

Can the children think of the problems which face animals in the winter?
Find out how different animals cope with colder weather and the scarcity of food and water (where water freezes).
They will know that some animals hibernate; ask them what else animals could do.
Can they find out how animals (which do not hibernate, migrate or die) survive?

Background information
Many animals eat more than they need in the autumn. They become noticeably fatter. The fur of many mammals becomes thicker before winter. Birds fluff up their feathers to act as insulation. Some animals spend winter in a part of their cycle where food is not needed, e.g. as eggs, larvae or pupae.

Animals in winter

Hibernate	Migrate	Die, but eggs hatch in Spring
snail squirrel frog	swallow caribou some moths and butterflies	housefly mayfly

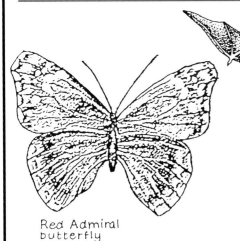

Red Admiral butterfly

North American bat

Curlew

Discussion

What do children think would happen if animals such as snails, which normally hibernate, were fed and kept warm?
Keep four or five snails in a seed propagator, in a warm place during the winter.
Keep their environment damp.
Feed them with lettuce, other leaves, cucumber and oatmeal mixed with water.

Tortoises and many mammals hibernate whatever the temperature, but grey squirrels do not hibernate in Britain.
Can the children think why?
(They find sufficient food near human habitation.)

Protecting wildlife

The survival of some animals is hindered by people. Their habitats are harmed or destroyed.
Find out about endangered species. What is being done to protect them? What do the children think they could do to help protect them?
If possible begin small conservation areas in the school grounds.

Activity sheet: Don't eat me!

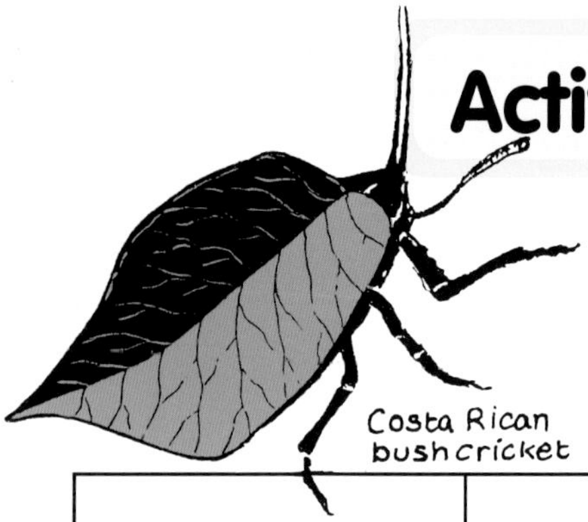

Costa Rican
bush cricket

Name: _____

This chart shows how some animals protect themselves.
● See if you can find out more about them.

Animal	How it protects itself from predators.				
	Frightens them	Makes a foul smell	Bright colour as a warning	Stings	Camouflage
Costa Rican bush cricket					●
bombadier beetle		●			
skunk		●			
golden arrow poison frog			●		
owl butterfly	●				
hornet				●	

● How does the bombadier beetle protect itself? _____

_____

● How does the Costa Rican bush cricket protect itself? _____

_____

● How many of the animals on the chart protect themselves by making foul smells?

_____

● Think of other ways that animals can protect themselves.
  Make a chart of your own for different animals.

Teachers' Notes. (Delete when photocopying.)
The children may think of more self defence mechanisms when making their own charts, e.g. scratching, kicking, biting, butting, running, flying, swimming or slithering away.

Birds

If possible visit a bird sanctuary, during different seasons. Watch birds in the school grounds, and encourage children to watch them near their homes. Where do they usually see the birds that they know? Watch different places for the same length of time.

Do they think that the time of year makes a difference to the bird visitors? Keep a long term record, using a chart or database.

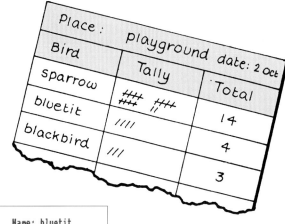

Bird	Tally	Total
sparrow	++++ ++++ ++++ ++	14
bluetit	////	4
blackbird	///	3

Place: playground date: 2 Oct

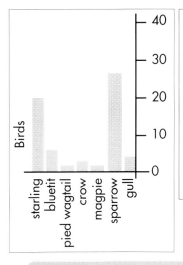

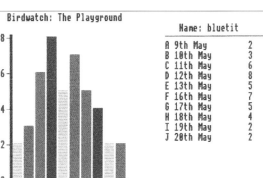

Birdwatch: The Playground

Name: bluetit

A	9th May	2
B	10th May	3
C	11th May	6
D	12th May	8
E	13th May	5
F	16th May	7
G	17th May	5
H	18th May	4
I	19th May	2
J	20th May	2

Birdwatching

Ensure that the children dress appropriately. Binoculars are useful. Encourage them to take notes and make sketches of birds. A hide, in the school grounds, could be useful. See if the children can make one. Never try to catch birds or collect eggs.

Discussion

Try to classify birds

Think about their size: small (sparrow size), large (swan or eagle size), or in between (crow size).

Look at their feet:
Look at their beaks:

flat bill
e.g. mallard

short and pointed
e.g. coot

webbed

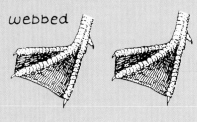

short and thin
e.g. thrush

not webbed

short and sharp

e.g. bluetit

short and thick

e.g. sparrow

Can you think of other ways you could classify them?

Activity sheet: Bird key

Name: _____

● Put these birds in their places on the key.

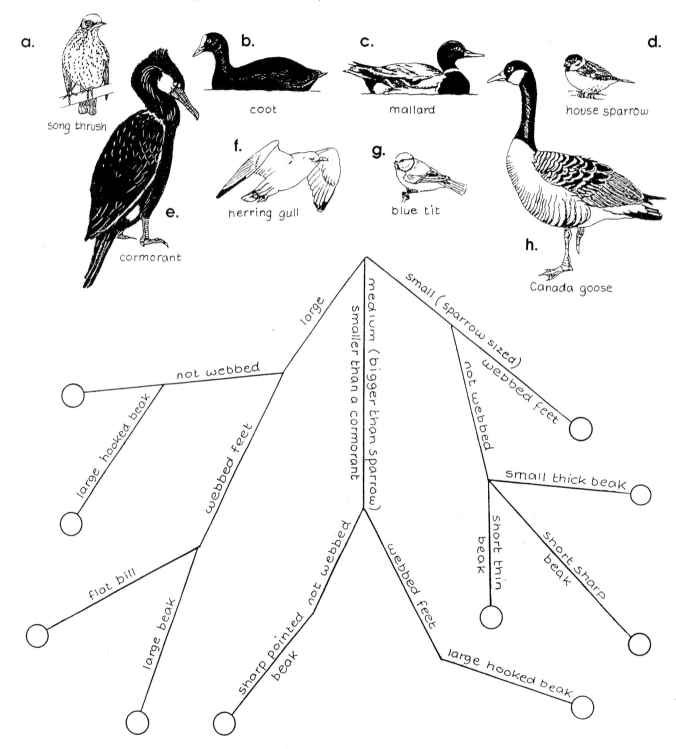

a. song thrush

b. coot

c. mallard

d. house sparrow

e. cormorant

f. herring gull

g. blue tit

h. Canada goose

large / small (sparrow sized)

medium (bigger than sparrow)

smaller than a cormorant

not webbed

webbed feet

large hooked beak

flat bill

large beak

sharp pointed not webbed beak

webbed feet

not webbed

webbed feet

small thick beak

short thin beak

short sharp beak

large hooked beak

Teachers' Notes. (Delete when photocopying.)
This branching key has been kept simple, therefore many possibilities have been omitted. Encourage the children to make their own keys and to add to this one.

SIA - Teachers' Resource Book 3. F2616